Construction technology volume 3

J. T. Grundy

BSc, AMICE, MBICSc
Lecturer in construction
Salford College of Technology

Edward Arnold

To Martin, Ray, and Jack

© J. T. Grundy 1981

First published 1981
by Edward Arnold (Publishers) Ltd
41 Bedford Square, London WC18 3DQ

ISBN 0 7131 3419 4

British Library Cataloguing in Publication Data

Grundy, J T
   Construction technology.
   Vol. 3
   1. Building
   I. Title
   690   TH145

   ISBN 0-7131-3419-4

Typeset by Reproduction Drawings Ltd, Sutton, Surrey, and printed in
Great Britain by R. Clay (Chaucer Press) Ltd, Bungay, Suffolk

Contents

Preface vi

Acknowledgements vi

1 **Soil investigation** 1
Site investigation. Scope of soil investigation. Methods of investigation.
Soil sampling. Site testing. Other important tests. Interpretation of
results. Outline site-investigation reports

2 **Site organisation** 10
Site-layout considerations. Accommodation layout. Bar charts. Site
personnel and relationships. Health, safety, and lifting regulations

3 **Excavation techniques** 18
Selection of plant. Earth-moving equipment. Basement excavation.
Basement construction. Water exclusion. Waterproofed concrete.
Service entry. Safety precautions in excavation. Selection of fill
material. Backfilling to retaining walls. Topsoil. Use of imported
fill

4 **Piling** 35
Sheet piling. Usage of sheet piles. Driving sheet piles. Sheet-pile
extraction. Piled foundations. Conditions for the use of piled
foundations. Pile construction

5 **Underpinning and dewatering** 46
Definition. Sequence of operations. Safety precautions. Reasons for
dewatering. Information for dewatering. Pumping from sumps. Land
drains

6 **Concrete work** 52
Choice of concreting plant. Quality control. Storage and mixing.
Types of plant. Reasons for curing. Methods of curing. Prestressed
concrete. Comparison with other materials

7 **Retaining walls and shoring** 61
Functions and stability of retaining walls. Typical retaining walls.
Shoring. Shoring materials and terminology. Erection and dismantling
of shoring

8   Scaffolding   71
Reasons for use. Scaffold types. Fittings

9   Framed structures   79
Steel sections. Bolted and welded joints. Steelwork connections.
Steelwork erection. Fire protection. Reinforcement of concrete.
Formwork. R.C. frame erection

10   Trussed roofs   98
Roof trusses. Steel trusses. Sheet roof covering. TRADA roof trusses.
Timber connectors

11   Walls   106
Brick panel walls. Lightweight panel walls. Concepts of cross-wall
construction. Constraints of cross-wall construction. Benefits of
cross-wall construction. Suitability of materials. Industrialised
methods. Special requirements of cross-walls

12   Windows   116
Metal windows. Patent glazing. Patent-glazing details

13   Suspended floors   120
Design criteria. Precast concrete floors. Provision of openings

14   Doors   124
Glazed double-swing doors. Fire-check doors

15   Partitions   128
Demountable partitions

16   Stairs   132
Open-riser stairs. Reinforced-concrete stairs

17   Linings   136
Dry lining. Building boards

18   Paintwork   140
Main defects. Causes. Remedies. Preparation

19   Heating systems   144
Small-bore systems. Controls

20   Electrical services   149
Electricity Board equipment. Cable sizing. Consumer's control gear.
Accessories. Cables. The ring-main system. Layouts

21   **Fireplaces and flues**   158
Open fireplaces. Flues and flue linings. Underfloor-draught control.
Gas fires and flues. Flue-block construction

22   **Gas services**   170
Gas Board intake. Typical gas installation

23   **Underground drainage**   175
Drain laying. Road drainage. Manhole construction. Comparison of
manhole-construction methods. Sewer connection. Safety

24   **Surface-water drainage**   182
Basis of calculations. Flow calculations

25   **Road construction**   185
Pavements. Terminology. Pavement strength. Subgrade strength.
Subgrade requirements. Road-construction materials. Pavement
construction. Road details

26   **Demolition**   192
Reasons for demolition. Statutory controls. Risks and protection.
Demolition methods. Temporary works

Index   *200*

Preface

The student should by now have come to appreciate that there are many solutions to any given constructional problem and that no two problems are the same, since the criteria to be met are many and varied.

In this third volume, the aims of the level-3 TEC Construction Technology units for both building and civil/structural-engineering technicians have been covered. For students wishing to adhere rigidly to either unit, the specific objectives relating to each have been highlighted at the beginning of each chapter by asterisks:

* building only   ** civil/structural engineering only

No asterisk indicates that the item is common to both units.

However, it is hoped that the student will widen his appreciation of the construction industry by reading all the material contained in the book.

Acknowledgements

The author again wishes to acknowledge the assistance he has received from his wife and from Ray Booth, Jack Hodson, and other colleagues during the preparation of this volume.

Copyright material in the form of extracts from the Building Regulations 1976, advisory leaflets and information, and figs 17.2, 17.3, and 26.4 relating to linings and demolition, together with extracts from other government publications, is reproduced by permission of the Controller of Her Majesty's Stationary Office.

Extracts from British Standards are reproduced by permission of the British Standards Institution, 2 Park Lane, London W1A 2BS, from whom copies of the complete standards can be obtained.

The author would also like to thank Alcan Windows Ltd, British Gypsum, Kwickform Ltd, Norwood Partitions Ltd, The Rawlplug Co. Ltd, TAC Construction Materials Ltd, TRADA, True Flue Ltd, and West's Piling and Construction Co. Ltd, for their kind assistance with information and diagrams.

J. T. Grundy

1 Soil investigation

Understands the necessity for and scope of soil investigation and prepares a site-investigation report.

* *1.1 Identifies the relationship between soil investigation and site investigation.*
*   1.2 States that the scope of soil investigation depends upon the size and type of structure.*
***1.3 Describes the methods and equipment necessary for carrying out site-investigation work, with the emphasis on the standard percussion method.*
*   1.4 Describes the collection of undisturbed and disturbed samples of soil for testing.*
***1.5 Describes site tests, with special emphasis on the standard penetration test and the CBR test.*
***1.6 Lists the procedures and explains the purpose of*
*   a) the grading test,*
*   b) the sulphate-content test.*
***1.7 Interprets borehole logs and soil-investigation reports.*
***1.8 Prepares an outline site-investigation report.*

Acknowledgement is due to the Technician Education Council for permission to use the content of the TEC units in this chapter. The council reserves the right to amend the content of its units at any time.

1.1 Site investigation

Site investigation, as the term implies, is the preliminary work carried out to establish the suitability of a proposed site for new construction works, to enable an adequate and economic design to be prepared for the foundations, and to attempt to foresee and provide against difficulties that may arise during construction due to ground or other local conditions. It involves an investigation of

a)   the topography of the site;
b)   the state of buildings on and adjoining the site;
c)   the location of buried services;
d)   the previous history and use of the site, including information about defects attributable to foundation conditions;
e)   the likelihood of earthquakes, flooding, seasonal ground movement, and soil erosion;
f)   underground mining activity (proposed, present, or past);
g)   the availability and quality of local materials and labour;
h)   information relating to tides, river levels, and the velocity and direction of water flow (for river and coastal works only);
j)   the general geology of the area, with particular reference to the major geological formations underlying the site;

k) the soil and rock strata together with ground-water conditions within the bulb(s) likely to be affected by foundation bearing pressures;
l) soil and rock samples in respect of their strength and chemical composition as they might affect the foundation design.

Of these, items (k) and (l) are commonly classed as soil investigation.

1.2 Scope of soil investigation

The amount of investigation into soil conditions carried out on a site depends to a large extent on the site and on the type of structure which is proposed. For small sites, the location and depth of bore or trial holes should be such as to build up a profile of those soils which are likely to affect the stability of the foundations. To this end, boreholes should extend to a depth at which the original foundation ground pressure should have reduced to some 20% of that original value. This depth will depend upon the type of foundation proposed, and a good guide is that the depth of investigation should extend at least 1.5 times the foundation width below the foundation level, see fig. 1.1.

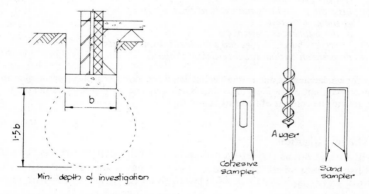

Fig. 1.1 Sampling devices

It should be noted that a strip foundation produces a larger pressure bulb than a pad foundation, due to its continuous nature, and that overlap stressing of the soil may occur where foundations are close together.

On large sites, investigation should again be carried out to establish the soil profile, but this is usually achieved by taking trial bores on a grid pattern with the option of extra bores to clarify any suspect areas or where complex operations are to be carried out.

1.3 Methods of investigation

The method of investigation, determined by the scope and the building type, can be broken down into those investigations carried out on site and those carried out in a laboratory.

2

The three general methods of investigation are (a) trial holes, (b) shallow boreholes, (c) deep boreholes.

a) *Trial holes* (see also volume 2, chapter 1) These allow a visual inspection of the strata and the taking of hand-cut soil samples which have a minimum disturbance factor, thereby enabling more accurate laboratory test results to be obtained. They are also more economic for shallow depths and enable in-situ load testing to be performed.

b) *Shallow boreholes* (see also volume 2, chapter 1) These are carried out using a hand auger and are suitable for depths up to 7 m in soft to firm soils which will stand unsupported.

c) *Deep boreholes* These are carried out using either a mechanical auger or a shell or percussion bore and are used for depths of up to 30 m.

  The mechanical auger (fig. 1.1) is used in gravelly types of soil in conjunction with a lining or casing to prevent the collapse of the borehole. The linings, in lengths varying from 0.6 m to 2 m, are screwed together and driven down as drilling proceeds.

  The shell boring tool consists of a cylindrical steel shell which is dropped into the soil, causing soil to be forced into the cylinder which is then withdrawn for removal of the soil. The soil is held in the cylinder either by friction in the case of cohesive soils or by a non-return flap in the case of non-cohesive soils.

  Percussion boring is the oldest form of boring and consists of breaking up the soil formation by repeated blows from a chisel or bit. Friction and heat are reduced by the introduction of water into the hole as the work proceeds. At intervals, the broken material is removed from the hole by a shell auger or by flushing using pressurised water jets. Samples of soil obtained by this method are not very reliable, due to their extremely disturbed nature.

Other methods of investigation include

d) *Wash boring*, where the soil (of small grain size) is removed from the borehole by the action of a strong jet of water injected through a steel tube, the debris being carried in suspension out of the hole between the jetting tube and the lining.

e) *Rotary boring* using special drills to investigate rock strata.

In each case, a record of the various types and depths of soil is kept. (A typical record is shown in volume 2, fig. 1.3.)

1.4 Soil sampling
Soil samples are classified as either (a) disturbed or (b) undisturbed.

a) *Disturbed samples* Samples which are brought to the surface when using boring tools are disturbed, since the natural structure of the material will have been modified or destroyed. Care should be taken to see that the sample is representative of the soil deposit and is of sufficient size to enable testing to be carried out. Figure 1.2 indicates typical sample sizes.

  Samples brought to the surface by a washing process should be allowed to settle in the form of a sludge in troughs.

Purpose of sample	Soil type	Mass of sample required (kg)
Soil identification and natural-moisture-content tests Chemical tests	Cohesive soils Gravels	0.7 3.0
Compaction tests	Cohesive soils and sands Gravelly soils	11.0 22.0
Comprehensive examinations of construction materials including soil stabilisation	Cohesive soils and sands Gravelly soils	22–45 45–90

Fig. 1.2   Soil sample-size requirements

Samples for testing should be immediately placed in airtight containers of approximately 0.5 kg capacity with little or no air inside the containers. The containers should be numbered, with a label placed inside each container immediately under the cover, and should then be carefully packed in wooden boxes to prevent damage in transit.

b) *Undisturbed samples*   These are samples which attempt to preserve the natural structure and properties of the material so that a better quantitative laboratory analysis may be made. They are generally taken from cohesive soils and rocks using a British Standard sampling tube (see fig. 1.3). The tube is screwed on to a length of rods and is pushed or driven into the soil. The detachable cutting shoe has an internal diameter which is 1 mm less than the inside of the sample tube, thereby reducing side friction and consolidation of the sample during driving. The sides of the tube may also be oiled to assist in friction reduction. The distance the tube has been driven is checked to ensure that the tube has been filled (the overdrive space in the head of the sampler allows complete filling without consolidation). After driving, the sampler is rotated to break off the core and is removed from the borehole. On removal, the sample tube is detached and the ends are sealed with molten wax or with rubber caps, thereby preserving the moisture content of the soil. The tube is numbered and suitably packed for transit.

Where clay is in an exposed excavation, such as a trial hole, hand samples may be taken by carefully removing a block of clay with a sharp knife and immediately placing it in a sealed container.

Sampling methods may be summarised as shown in fig. 1.4.

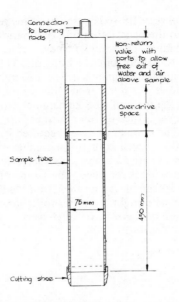

Connection to boring rods

Non-return valve with ports to allow free exit of water and air above sample

Overdrive space

Sample tube

75 mm

450 mm

Cutting shoe

Fig. 1.3 British Standard sampling tube

Nature of ground	Type of sample	Method of sampling
Soil	Disturbed	Hand samples Auger samples (in clays) Shell samples (in sands)
	Undisturbed	Hand samples Core samples
Rock	Disturbed	Sludge samples from percussion or rotary drills
	Undisturbed	Hand samples Cores

Fig. 1.4 Methods of sampling

1.5 Site testing

In-situ testing has the major advantage of testing the soil in a completely un-disturbed state, particularly in soils such as sands and silts where undisturbed samples are difficult or expensive to obtain. BS 1377:1975 specifies twenty-one standard methods of testing soils, the majority being carried out in the laboratory but a few being specifically for in-situ testing.

a) *Standard penetration test* (BS 1377 test 19) This test determines the resistance of a soil to the penetration of a split-barrel sampler under static or dynamic loading. The sampler, shown in fig. 1.5, is attached to rods and is lowered to the bottom of a borehole. The drive assembly is connected to rods, and the sampler is driven 150 mm into the soil by a series of standard blows, the number of blows required being recorded. (A standard blow is the force of a 65 kg hammer dropping 760 mm vertically.) The sampler is then driven a further 300 mm or an additional 50 standard blows. The number of blows required for each 75 mm of penetration is recorded as well as the total number of blows for the full 300 mm penetration. Where 50 blows are struck after the initial drive, the amount of penetration is recorded. The sampler is then removed and opened, and a soil core sample is removed from the bottom 300 mm section and placed in an airtight container for laboratory analysis. The test gives an indication of the relative soil density: the fewer the number of blows, the looser or softer the soil.

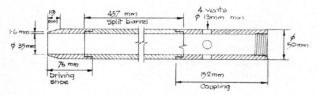

Fig. 1.5 Split-barrel sampler

b) *California bearing ratio (CBR) test* (BS 1377 test 16) This British Standard test is designed to be carried out in the laboratory, but site testing may also be performed along similar lines. The CBR test derives from work done by the California Division of Highways in the late 1920's to assist in determining the strength of soils for highway-design purposes. The test consists of the measurement of the force/penetration relationship of a cylindrical plunger in the soil as compared to the same relationship for a standard crushed-stone sample, the results being expressed as a percentage. On site this may be carried out using a jack, a load cell, and kentledge in the form of a waggon axle, the soil under test being generally 1 m below ground level in order to avoid problems resulting from the effects of moisture-content variation.

Other site tests on soils include:

c) *Plate bearing test* A 600 mm square plate is place horizontally on the soil at the level of the proposed foundation and is loaded with weights or by means of a jack and kentledge, see fig. 1.6. The rate and amount of loading having been predetermined, a record of the plate's settlement is kept. Loading is continued until either a predetermined settlement has been reached or the load is in excess of three times the design load of the proposed foundation.

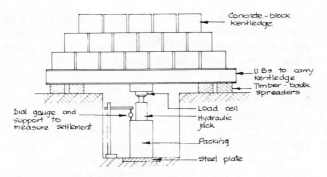

Fig. 1.6 Plate bearing test

d) *Vane test* (BS 1377 test 18) Used to determine the shear strength of soils — generally clays — the test is carried out using a standard vane (fig. 1.7) which is attached to rods and lowered down a borehole. The vane is pushed into the soil at the bottom to at least three times the borehole diameter and a torque is applied to the rods until the soil shears. The amount of torque required is recorded and is directly proportional to the shear strength of the soil.

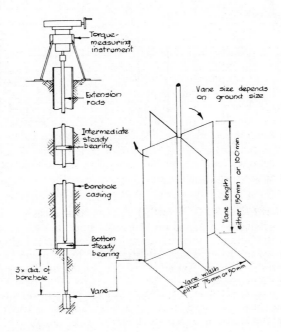

Fig. 1.7 Vane test

7

e) *Unconfined compression test* (BS 1377 test 20)   Standard soil samples, 38 mm diameter and 75 mm long, are individually placed in a portable apparatus and are compressed. The load and deformation are automatically recorded on a chart until the sample shears.

1.6 Other important tests

a) *Grading test* (BS 1377 test 7)   A knowledge of the particle-size distribution of a soil not only assists in the identification of the soil but also is of use for (i) the selection of suitable fill material, (ii) the choice of method for artificially stabilising a non-cohesive soil, (iii) identifying problems of erosion and silting, (iv) assessing the suitability of the material as an aggregate, (v) determining the permeability of the soil.

The grading test is carried out by passing a soil sample through a series of BS test sieves which are agitated. The amount of the sample retained on each sieve is weighed, and a cumulative graph is prepared showing the percentage (by mass) of the sample passing through each sieve.

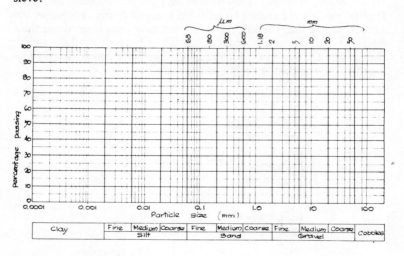

Fig. 1.8   Particle-size distribution chart

b) *Sulphate-content test* (BS 1377 test 9)   Chemical analysis of the soil is another important aspect of soil investigation, since harmful chemicals may damage the building substructure and services. This is particularly so in the case of sulphates, which can attack and break down OPC concrete, thus requiring a more expensive type of concrete manufacture with sulphate-resisting cement.

This test is carried out in a laboratory and begins with the total drying and sieving through a 2 mm BS test sieve of the sample. A 100 g sample of the sieved material is then pulverised and passed through a 425 μm BS test sieve. A 10 g sample of the material passing through this sieve is

8

taken and redried. 2 g of this latter sample is then taken and — using various reagents in conjunction with boiling, filtration, and burning — a pure sulphate precipitate is obtained from which the total sulphate content of the soil (expressed as a percentage) can be obtained.

1.7 Interpretation of results

From the borehole logs, profiles of the soil can be prepared which enable a detailed picture of the soil strata to be built up. From these and the soil-investigation report(s) the foundation engineer is able to determine the type and level of foundation required for the intended structure, while the contractor is able to appreciate the difficulties which will face him during the period that foundation construction is proceeding as well as any constraints which may be imposed on him contractually by the designer.

1.8 Outline site-investigation reports

The site-investigation report should incorporate the following:
a) *Introduction*   This will state the client, the work carried out, the site name, and other terms of reference.
b) General *site description* in terms of topography, location, and aspect.
c) The general *geology* of the area, obtained from
    i)   topographical inspection of the site and its vicinity,
    ii) geological survey maps and memoirs.
d) A *description of the site subsoil* as identified from boreholes etc., together with borehole logs.
e) The *laboratory and site test results.*
f) *Comments on the results* and their effect on all matters pertaining to the proposed works.
g) *Conclusions and recommendations* on all aspects of the design in the light of the results and comments of (e) and (f) above.

2   Site organisation

Understands the necessity for organising, laying out, and arranging access to sites in a logical and orderly manner.

2.1   *Describes and relates the main factors to be considered in laying out a new site.*

2.2   *Lists the principal factors which affect the layout of materials, storage facilities, and workshops on site.*

**2.3   *Uses bar-chart programmes for contract and site planning.*

**2.4   *Explains the needs of the members of the contractor's site team and outlines the relationship between the engineer and the contractor.*

**2.5   *Describes the scope of regulations with reference to*
    a) health and safety,
    b) lifting.

Acknowledgement is due to the Technician Education Council for permission to use the content of the TEC units in this chapter. The council reserves the right to amend the content of its units at any time.

The statement 'A tidy site indicates a well run site' implies that the organisation both on and off the site should be well planned, which in turn implies that the economic potential of the work is likely to be fully realised. By careful planning, both during the work period and before its commencement, wastage of resources in terms of materials and manpower can be reduced to a minimum.

2.1 Site-layout considerations

Before any work is begun on site, the contractor must consider various preliminary items which will inevitably influence all future site operations. The major factors to be considered are

a)   access,
b)   storage,
c)   plant and movement of plant,
d)   temporary site-accommodation requirements and location of huts,
e)   temporary services,
f)   fencing and hoardings.

a)   *Access*   There are two components to this factor: (i) access to the site itself and (ii) access on the site. In the first case there may be limitations imposed by the locality of the site, such as road widths, weight and parking restrictions, traffic density and bridge weights, or other environmental considerations such as noise levels and other nuisance problems.

Each of these may affect the choice of vehicle and method of delivery of goods and materials both to and from the site. In case (ii), once the materials or vehicles have reached the site there should be ready access to the various working areas or stores so that there is no time lost in waiting for items to be dealt with. This may necessitate the construction of temporary roadways or the early partial completion of permanent carriageways.

b) *Storage* There are many forms and methods of storage available to the contractor (see volume 2, section 2.7). In laying out a new site, the object should be to reduce any multiple handling of materials to a minimum, commensurate with cost factors, while ensuring that stored materials are secure but readily available when required. Stores should therefore be located such that they do not interfere with any work in progress but are readily accessible for both the deposit and removal of goods.

c) *Plant* The contractor's plant policy will to a large extent determine the selection of items of plant. The utilisation of his own equipment, even if it is not the ideal item for executing a particular operation, may dictate the type of plant on site; whereas adopting a hiring policy will permit specialised items of plant to be brought on to the site to give maximum output under specific working conditions. Many multi-purpose machines are now available, and these provide a degree of flexibility in site-layout considerations (e.g. loader—excavators, fork-lift trucks, etc.).

Plant movement must be considered from three points of view:
 i) working-room requirements,
 ii) mobility on site,
 iii) servicing requirements.

 i) Many excavating and lifting items of plant have slewing circles which extend outside their tracking requirements. This working room must be considered when selecting an item of plant for a particular purpose, especially in confined areas.
 ii) Plant mobility should be such as not to reduce the efficient working of the site as a whole.

 Plant such as cranes may be static, semi-mobile (on tracks), or mobile, and selection should be based on optimum site coverage with minimum down-time. Excavators have varying turning circles, while most earth-moving vehicles require reasonably firm running surfaces (see (a) above).
 iii) Most items of plant require some form of servicing (other than maintenance), whether it be a power supply for electric cranes, hoists, or hand tools, or back-up vehicles in the form of dumpers for a batching plant, waggons for an excavator, or wheelbarrows for a hoist. In each instance the siting and spatial requirements must be taken into account when laying out a site.

d) *Temporary accommodation* As was stated in volume 2, section 2.5, the size and amount of accommodation on a site will vary depending on the

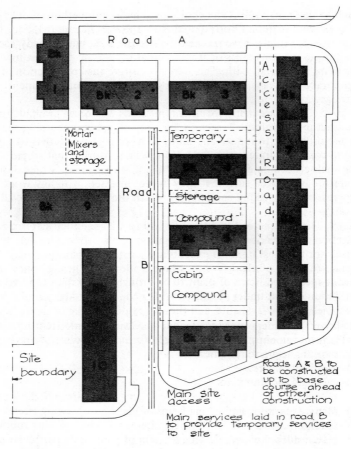

Road A

Bk 1

Bk 2

Bk 3

Access Road

Bk

Bk 7

Mortar Mixers and storage

Temporary

Bk

Road B

Storage

Compound

Bk 9

Cabin

Compound

Bk

Site boundary

Main site access

Roads A & B to be constructed up to base course ahead of other construction

Main services laid in road B to provide Temporary services to site

Fig. 2.1 Typical Site Layout

circumstances, although certain accommodation is statutorily required and the client may also specify size and type of accommodation and fittings for his own staff in the contract documents.

The location of the accommodation will depend on the availability of space within the site boundary and the proximity of services to such accommodation. In restricted city-centre sites, accommodation may be provided at a level above pavement areas, subject to the approval of the local authority.

e) *Temporary services* Wherever possible, the provision of temporary services should be tied in with the future permanent service connections to the site, so that little or no additional cost is incurred. The temporary service runs from the existing or new permanent service locations should be as short as possible. Early consultation with the statutory authorities on such provisions can avoid later frustration when work on site is begun.

f) *Fencing and hoardings* The provision of some form of site protection may be specified in contract documents; alternatively, the contractor must consider such requirements in the light of the security requirements outlined in volume 2, section 2.3. Access and exit points are, however, generally located according to the contractor's discretion and should be in such positions as to provide a free flow for vehicular traffic while maintaining a suitable level of security.

2.2 Accommodation layout
a) *Materials* The factors which affect the location of materials are
   i) space availability;
   ii) location in relation to plant, e.g. concrete mixer;
   iii) effect on other work;
   iv) ease of loading and off-loading;
   v) effect on the smooth flow of site traffic.
b) *Storage facilities* These are located having consideration to
   i) space availability;
   ii) ease of loading and off-loading;
   iii) ease of issuing materials;
   iv) security;
   v) conformity with regulations, e.g. for petrol and derv;
   vi) effect on the smooth flow of site traffic.
c) *Workshops* These may be for site prefabrication operations, e.g. carpentry, plumbing, concreting, etc., or for plant maintenance. Factors affecting their location include
   i) proximity to site services;
   ii) ease of access for plant;
   iii) proximity to office accommodation and surrounding buildings in respect of noise;
   iv) space availability;
   v) effect on the smooth flow of site traffic.

It can be seen from the foregoing that the principal factors in any site layout are space availability and the smooth working of the site.

2.3 Bar charts
In any work operation, planning is essential if delays are to be avoided. The first requirement is the identification of the operations involved, followed by quantifying items and subsequently allotting a duration of time to the operation. This duration will depend on the method of working and time constants derived from either previous experience or work study.

The bar chart is a simple graphical method of representing this information in a sequence such that problems may be identified and remedied — see fig. 2.2. Bar charts are used for
a) *pre-tender planning*, so that a method statement can be prepared and the estimator can accurately forecast labour and plant costs together with the cost of preliminary items and supervision;
b) *pre-contract planning*, so that material ordering can provide correct

13

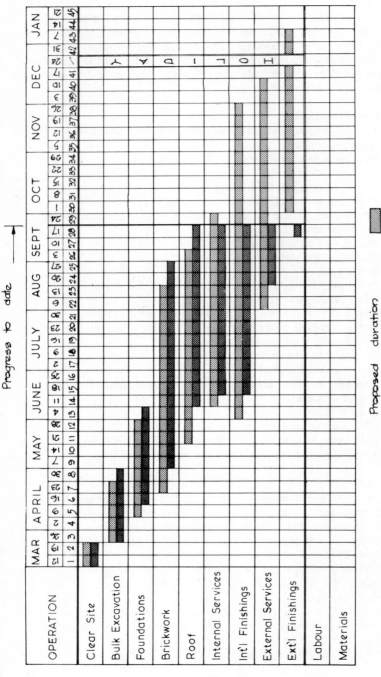

Fig. 2.2. Bar Chart Programme

14

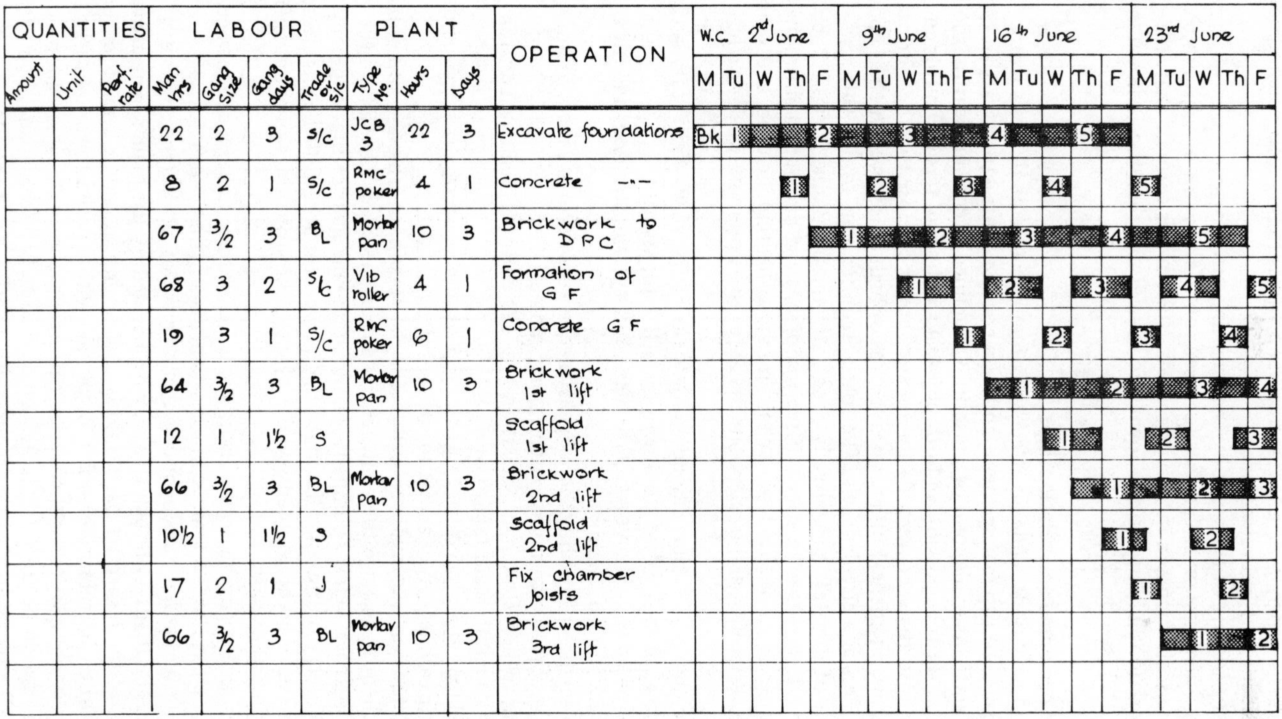

Fig. 2.3 Stage programme

Amount	Unit	Rate	Man hrs	Gang size	Gang shop	Trade o/s	Pl/Eqt	Hours	shop	OPERATION	W.C. 2nd June		9th June		16th June		23rd June	
			22	2	3	s/c	JCB 3	22	3	Excavate foundations								
			8	2	1	s/c	RMC poker	4	1	Concrate "								
			67	3/2	3	BL	Mortar pan	10	3	Brickwork to DPC								
			68	3	2	s/c	Vib roller	4	1	Formation of GF								
			19	3	1	s/c	RMC poker	6	1	Concrete GF								
			64	3/2	3	BL	Mortar pan	10	3	Brickwork 1st lift								
			12	1	1½	S				Scaffold 1st lift								
			66	3/2	3	BL	Mortar pan	10	3	Brickwork 2nd lift								
			10½	1	1½	S				Scaffold 2nd lift								
			17	2	1	J				Fix chamber joists								
			66	3/2	3	BL	Mortar pan	10	3	Brickwork 3rd lift								

Fig. 2.3 Stage programme

quantities and timing of arrival on site;

c) *a master programme* on which actual progress can be recorded and delays be identified and remedied;

d) *cost planning* of the work by the quantity surveyor;

e) *stage planning* on site, either for a section of the work or for a limited time-scale such as a month or a week. N.B., in this form of chart the operations will be broken down into more detail than those shown in fig. 2.2 (see fig. 2.3).

2.4 Site personnel and relationships

Site productivity depends on effective communication at all levels from labour force to top management, and between the contractor's staff and the client's staff. As in all good organisations, the lines of communication should be kept as short as possible in both physical and human terms. To this end, the administrative accommodation on site should be close together for both contractor and client, but away from areas of high noise levels such as concrete mixers and circular saws. The spatial requirements for the various members of site staff have already been indicated in volume 2, fig. 2.2, but other requirements in terms of office equipment and back-up facilities may be required as follows (a desk, a chair, means of heating, lighting, and ventilation, power points, and a telephone being taken as prerequisite for each office):

a) Site manager – filing cabinet, additional chairs, view of site, easy access to site, good site directioning to his office for visitors.

b) Site engineer – drawing board, plan-filing system, surveying instruments, secure storage, chainman.

c) Foreman – plan-filing system, easy access to workmen's mess room.

d) Surveyors – plan-filing system, filing cabinets.

e) Timekeeper, storeman – location near site entrance, ready access for workmen, first-aid facilities.

f) Resident engineer, clerk of works – plan-filing system, drawing board, filing cabinets, easy access to site and site manager.

By definition, the engineer/architect is the person or company appointed by the client to manage the contract and act on the client's behalf. In the case of the 'engineer' being a company, an individual member of that company will be appointed to act with full or specified powers on behalf of the engineer. The contractor is the company whose offer to carry out the works has been accepted by the client.

In practice, a good working relationship between engineer and contractor is developed at site level between the site manager (the contractor's site representative) and the resident engineer or clerk of works (the engineer's site representative), although this may be affected by the higher management attitudes of the respective parties. This relationship should be one of mutual respect for each other's viewpoint, combined with a desire to see an early and satisfactory completion to the works. Unfortunately this ideal is seldom achieved, due to personality clashes which lead to bad feeling and, in extreme cases, to the removal of one of the disputing parties from the site.

16

2.5 Health, safety, and lifting regulations

The regulations concerning site conditions now come under the Health and Safety at Work Act 1974, which in turn embodies the Construction Regulations of 1961 and 1966.

a) *Health and Safety*   The Act places a general duty on employers to ensure the health, safety, and welfare at work of their employees; to consult them concerning arrangements for joint action on health and safety matters and in prescribed circumstances, at the request of duly appointed safety representatives, to establish safety committees; and to prepare and publicise written safety policy statements and arrangements. The Act also places a duty on employees to take reasonable care in ensuring that they do not endanger either themselves or other persons who may be affected by their work activities.

    The regulations cover accommodation, sanitation, protective clothing, first aid, fire prevention, dangerous materials (such as asbestos), liquefied petroleum gases, scaffolding, tunnelling, excavation, working over water, site electricity, welding, materials handling, hand power tools, and other mechanical equipment. Compliance with the regulations and safe working procedures, while incumbent on the employee, are the responsibility of the foreman and ultimately of the site manager. Weekly inspections and records are required for many of the above items and, where accidents occur, formal recording and reporting procedures are laid down.

b) *Lifting*   There are many forms of lifting devices and components which may be used on a site, ranging from hoists for both materials and men, through the various types of cranes to gin wheels, slings, hooks, ropes, and chains. In the main they should be tested before use and be inspected at regular intervals by suitably qualified personnel, with suitable records being kept, all in accordance with the Construction (Lifting Operations) Regulations 1961.

3 Excavation techniques

Understands the techniques, procedures, and plant involved in large-scale earth movement and basement excavation and construction, including integral and applied methods of waterproofing.

3.1 *Identifies the factors which influence the choice of earth-moving equipment and excavating methods.*

3.2 *Describes types of earth-moving equipment.*

*3.3 *Sketches and describes methods of excavating basements in various ground conditions.*

*3.4 *Sketches and describes basement construction using concrete and brick retaining walls.*

*3.5 *Describes and illustrates methods and provisions for excluding water from basement structures:*
  a) mastic-asphalt tanking and protection,
  b) proprietary tanking,
  c) watertight concrete.

*3.6 *Describes and illustrates the main provisions for waterproofed-concrete construction:*
  a) additives and plasticisers to reduce permeability and aid workability without loss of strength in the concrete,
  b) joint design and use of water-stops of various types and materials,
  c) quality control of concrete and provision for meeting specification requirements.

*3.7 *Describes and illustrates methods of providing for services access within basements.*

3.8 *Describes the precautions to be taken during excavations to ensure safe working.*

**3.9 *Describes the factors which affect the choice of materials for filling and levelling.*

**3.10 *Describes backfilling procedures to foundations and retaining walls.*

**3.11 *Describes the reuse of topsoil on site.*

**3.12 *Describes the use of imported backfill materials on site.*

Acknowledgement is due to the Technician Education Council for permission to use the content of the TEC units in this chapter. The council reserves the right to amend the content of its units at any time.

3.1 Selection of plant

Earth moving involves not only excavation but also transportation, tipping, and filling, and there are many factors which will influence the selection of earth-moving equipment. They may be classified as follows.

a) *Physical*
  i) Volume of earth to be excavated.

ii) Limits of the work — the constraints imposed by the site layout and its surrounds which may affect working space.

iii) Depth of excavation.

iv) Nature of the subsoil — the difficulty of excavating and the amount of bulking.

v) Height of water table.

vi) Method of disposal of excavated material — side cast or cart away.

vii) Distance to disposal point.

b) *Mechanical*

i) Method of plant operation — high-level, surface, or low-level.

ii) Plant function — single or multiple role, e.g. excavate and tip, or excavate, transport, and tip.

iii) Capacity of equipment.

iv) Speed of operation.

c) *Time*

i) Programmed duration of excavation works.

ii) Availability of plant to suit programme.

d) *Cost*

i) Decision to hire or buy equipment.

ii) Working conditions — down-time resulting from weather and the type of soil.

iii) Running and maintenance, including spares and labour.

iv) Transporting equipment to site.

e) *Method*

The method of excavation will depend upon a large number of the foregoing factors, together with an individual contractor's preference based on previous experience and company policy. Other factors which will affect the method of excavation are the proposed sequence of the subsequent construction operations and their programmed starting date, the method of ground support, and the provision of other safe working conditions.

3.2 Earth-moving equipment

Earth movement is the process of excavation and relocation, either temporarily or permanently, of soil. Large-scale earth movement, as encountered on a large housing site or new road construction, will require the production, initially, of a mass—haul diagram (fig. 3.1) which indicates the various volumes of excavation and fill together with the haul distances involved. Using this diagram, a decision can be made on the type of equipment suitable for carrying out the work.

The equipment may be categorised as follows.

a) Excavators (fig. 3.2) In most instances the excavators incorporate a short-range haul for tipping or depositing purposes.

i) *Universal excavator* This consists of a power unit which operates numerous pieces of equipment by means of ropes or hydraulics. The unit and the driver's cab are set on a 360° slewing ring which in turn is set

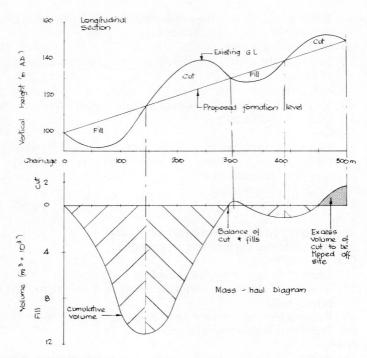

Fig. 3.1 Mass—haul diagram

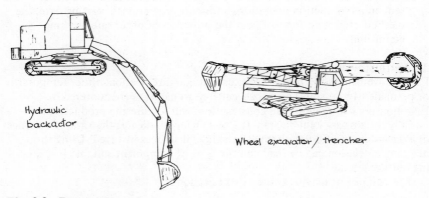

Hydraulic backactor

Wheel excavator / trencher

Fig. 3.2 Excavators

above caterpillar tracks for on-site mobility. Equipment available includes backactor, face shovel, grab, drag line, skimmer (see volume 1, fig. 5.2), crane, and pile-driving rig.

20

ii) *Trencher* Used to excavate long narrow trenches for pipelines, the trencher uses multiple buckets either attached to a large-diameter wheel at the front of the machine or on an endless chain supported by a boom at the rear of the machine.

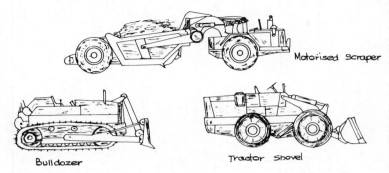

Motorised scraper

Bulldozer

Tractor shovel

Fig. 3.3 Excavator/carriers

b) Excavator/carriers (fig. 3.3) These machines are designed to excavate and carry earth for distances up to medium range.

i) *Scraper* May be motorised or tractor-drawn and is classified by the carrying capacity, which ranges from 5 m^3 to 50 m^3. The economic haul distances range from 300 m to 2 km, depending on the machine.

ii) *Bulldozer* Excavates to depths of 300 mm and pushes the earth up to 100 m. The blade may be raised and lowered by cables or hydraulics and may also be angled or tilted to suit particular requirements. The machine can also be used to tow a scraper using a hydraulic winch, or break up hard ground by means of a ripper.

iii) *Tractor shovel* Propelled on tracks or rubber tyres, various bucket operations are available, the 'four-in-one' being the most widely used machine because the four operations of dozing, grabbing, levelling, and loading can be carried out.

The above equipment is sometimes classified by the means of travel, i.e. tracked or wheeled. Tracked equipment while providing a stable base, has limited mobility, particularly between sites, when a low-loader must be provided. Wheeled equipment is more manoeuvrable, especially in poor or wet ground and between sites — see fig. 3.4 for these and other comparisons.

c) Carriers In general these consist of lorries and dump trucks, although conveyor belts or narrow-gauge railway may be used in special conditions such as headroom restriction.

i) *Lorries* Used for carting to tip, the lorry is designed for travel on the highways or on reasonable level firm ground.

ii) *Dump trucks* These are capable of carrying up to 50 m^3 and are designed for work on rough and uneven sites rather than on public highways.

21

Type	Means of travel	Turning circle/ slewing range	Machine standing	Depth range	Tip range	Bucket capacity (m³)	Output (buckets per hour)	General use
Backactor	Track	360°	G.L.	−15 m	12 m	0.3–3.0	60	Trenching
	Wheel	180°	G.L.	− 7 m	6 m	0.1–1.0	50	Trenching
Drag line	Track	360°	G.L.	−20 m	20 m	0.3–3.0	60	Bulk excavation
							30	R.L. excavation
Face shovel	Track	360°	Below working level	+10 m	9 m	0.3–3.0	70	Quarrying
Loader	Track	7 m	G.L.	± 3 m	10 m	0.6–2.0	50	R.L. excavation
	Wheel	10–15 m	G.L.	± 3 m	20 m	1.2–5.0	50	Loading
Trencher	Wheel		G.L.	−20 m				Bulk excavation
	Chain		G.L.	− 5 m			2 m/min forward travel	Trenching
Scraper	Wheel	10 m	G.L.	−0.4 m	7–20 m	7.0–20.0	100 m³/h	Bulk or R.L. excavation
Dozer	Track	6 m	G.L.	−0.4 m	30 m	0.8–10.0	80 m³/h	Grading
	Wheel	10 m	G.L.	−0.3 m	20 m	0.6–6.0	65 m³/h	and filling
Grab	Track	360°	G.L.	−30 m	15 m	0.1–3.0	30	Shaft
	Wheel	360°	G.L.	−20 m	15 m	0.1–3.0	30	excavation

Fig. 3.4 Comparison of excavators

iii) *Grader* This machine, most commonly found in motorised form but may be towed by tractor, is used to shape accurately embankments and formations by pushing the subsoil with a long centre-slung blade, rather than carrying.

3.3 Basement excavation

A basement is generally considered to be a storey or storeys below the ground-floor level or below the level of the surrounding finished ground.

The construction of a basement by excavation implies the removal of subsoil, and this factor must be borne in mind when the construction method is selected. Such work is most frequently carried out in city centres where other factors such as stability of adjacent buildings, proximity of services, and depth of foundation must be considered. However, the nature of the subsoil is the most important factor, since it will affect both the safety and speed of the operation.

Basements may be excavated in one of three ways, each being varied to suit specific site factors.

a) *Open excavation* The excavation is carried out for the full area, the sides of the excavation being battered back to the angle of repose of the subsoil. This method requires a large amount of space around the construction for the over-excavation but does not require any timbering, thus the costs of over-excavation and subsequent backfilling must be set against the saving in timbering support work. This form of excavation may also permit the use of surface excavators, with lorries gaining access to the working level by means of ramps in the sides of the cutting.

Open excavation does not depend on soil type but is dependent upon the water table being kept below the level of the excavation for stability and ease of working.

b) *Closed excavation* In reasonably firm soils the majority of the excavation can be carried out within the basement area from either ground or a lower level as in (a) above, without the use of temporary ground support. The final trimming up to the perimeter (allowance being made for external working room) is carried out either

   i) after construction of the majority of the base slab (fig. 3.5), in which case the slab may be used to provide anchorage for the raking struts; or

   ii) before construction, by trimming the perimeter and placing poling boards as the work proceeds, the raking struts being anchored into the formation.

A further variation is to drive sheet piles around the perimeter prior to excavation and subsequently install walings and struts as the excavation proceeds, or anchor the piles back to the existing ground at high level where working room permits. This method is frequently employed in loose or weak soils.

c) *Trench or dumpling method* An alternative method for weak soils is to excavate a perimeter trench with suitable timbering. The width of the trench should be sufficient to construct the basement walls and their

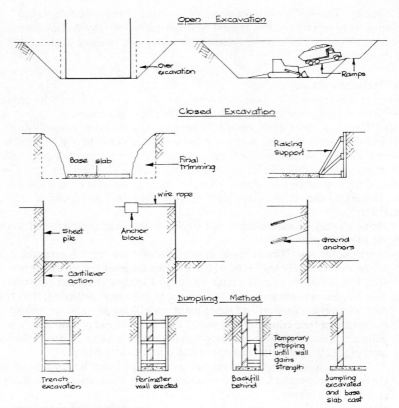

Fig. 3.5 Basement excavation

foundations, and these will subsequently act as retaining walls while the central section of the excavation is completed. A variation of this method is to use diaphragm walls (section 7.2(d)) which perform the same function.

The depth of the basement excavation may determine the type of excavator to be used. The maximum depth to which a backactor can reach is limited by its boom, and in deep excavations this may necessitate either excavation in two or more depth stages or the use of a drag line. However, a drag line cannot easily cut a vertical face and is more suited to the method outlined in (a) above. An alternative is to use a tractor shovel, but this requires the removal of the subsoil from low level by lorry, elevator, or crane and skip, thereby increasing plant costs.

3.4 Basement construction
The construction of a basement will depend on the size of the basement, its proximity to other structures, the structural design, and the nature of the subsoil.

The floor of the basement will usually provide a raft foundation at low level for the overall structure, as well as acting as a base or foundation to the perimeter walls and any internal load-bearing walls or columns.

Perimeter walls must generally resist both soil and ground-water pressures, as well as transmitting the loads from the superstructure to the foundation. The basement walls are, therefore, retaining walls forming an integral unit of basement construction.

The method of excavation of the basement will dictate whether the basement slab or the wall is the first to be constructed (section 3.3), but, whichever method is adopted, it is essential that the two components are properly linked together.

Details of the construction are given in section 3.5.

3.5 Water exclusion

The basement area, being in contact with the surrounding ground, will be subject to moisture penetration unless particular attention is paid to this problem. The easiest method of overcoming this is to prevent the structure becoming subject to ground-water pressure, and this may be achieved by reducing the water-table level below that of the basement by using perimeter land drains (fig. 3.6). However, this method may not be suitable where it is likely to cause settlement of surrounding buildings.

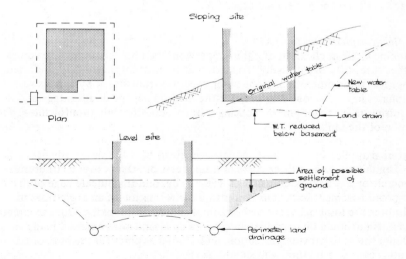

Fig. 3.6 Land drains

Basement walls can be protected from ground-water attack by the creation of a 'dry area' surrounding the structure (fig. 3.7), but this causes unusable space around the building.

25

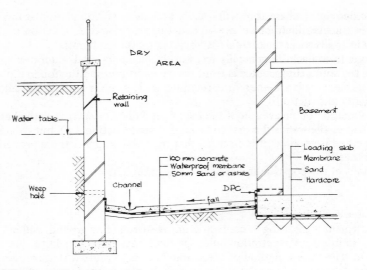

Fig. 3.7 Dry area to basement

Where the soil is in direct contact with the basement, some form of water-proof or damp-proof construction must be used (British Standard Code of Practice CP 102 gives detailed procedures).

a) Mastic-asphalt tanking

Tanking is the application of a thin impervious membrane around a structure, either externally or internally. The external application is generally preferred since it affords protection to the main structure from attack by aggressive sulphates in the surrounding soil, but the method has the disadvantage of requiring at least 600 mm of working room around the structure for the application of the tanking.

External application (fig. 3.8)   Mastic asphalt to BS 1418 or BS 1097 is laid horizontally in two or three coats to a thickness of 30 mm over a structural concrete base which extends at least 150 mm beyond the outside edge of the proposed basement wall, thus permitting the formation of an angle fillet to reinforce the joint between the horizontal and vertical tanking. Once complete, the asphalt should be immediately covered by a sand and cement screed, 50 mm thick, to provide protection, and as soon as practical the horizontal loading coat or structural slab should be cast.

After erection of the structural wall, a 20 mm thickness of vertical tanking is applied in three coats, care being taken to ensure that there is a sufficient key to support the asphalt. Brickwork and blockwork joints should be raked out, while concrete should have either a rough finish from timber-board shutters or a surface application of bonding agent. The top of the vertical tanking should be taken to a height at least 150 mm above ground level and

26

be turned into a chase at least 25 mm × 25 mm. The reinforcing fillet at the external angle should be at least 50 mm wide and formed in two coats. As soon as the vertical tanking has been applied it should be protected against damage from backfilling by a brick or blockwall built clear of the asphalt face, the void being grouted solidly with mortar, course by course.

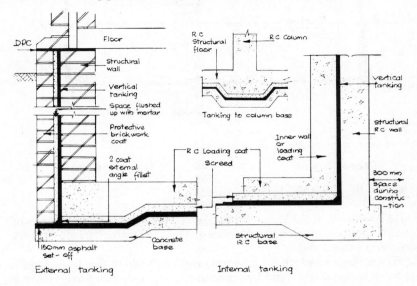

Fig. 3.8 Asphalt tanking

Internal application (fig. 3.8) After construction of the structural base and the external walls, the horizontal tanking is laid and the fillets are formed. A protective screed is again laid, and the vertical tanking is applied in a similar manner to external tanking. (Ideally there should be a 300 mm wide void outside the external wall, to prevent the wall becoming damp before the tanking is applied.) Where the internal loading slab and the walls are constructed of in-situ concrete, the walls should preferably be cast directly against the tanking. Where brick loading walls are used, they should be set 40 mm away from the tanking, thus preventing trowel damage, and the void should be grouted solidly, course by course, to ensure close contact between the loading wall and the asphalt.

The loading slab and walls must be designed to withstand the maximum ground-water pressure, thus preventing the asphalt being forced away from the structural slab and walls with resulting membrane fracture.

b) Bitumen-sheet tanking (fig. 3.9)
Instead of mastic-asphalt tanking, bitumen sheeting conforming to BS 743 class A may be used, each layer having a minimum mass of 3.8 kg/m² for

27

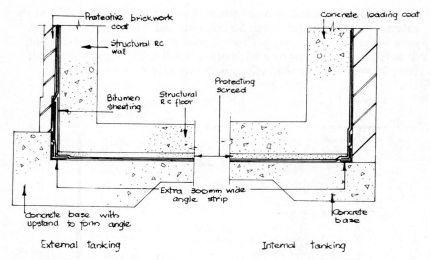

Fig. 3.9 Bitumen-sheet tanking

three-layer work or 5.4 kg/m² for two-layer work. The general principles of construction and protection are similar to those for mastic asphalt, with the following exceptions.

The surfaces to which the tanking is applied should be free from ridges and indentations; clean; and free from dust, sand, and other foreign material. For external tanking, the base should extend at least 225 mm beyond the outside edges of the structural wall.

Where bonding is required, a priming coat of bitumen solution or bitumen emulsion should be uniformly applied to the surface. When this is dry, the first layer of sheeting is bonded to the surface with bitumen compound at a temperature of approximately 190 °C, by pouring and rolling. Joints between sheets should have 150 mm end laps and 100 mm side laps. Further layers should be applied in a similar manner as soon as possible after one another.

c) Watertight concrete
This form of basement construction can be achieved only if (i) there is no cracking in the concrete, (ii) construction joints between the various sections of the work are watertight, and (iii) the concrete is impervious.

If no cracking of the structure is to occur, the basement structure must act monolithically, with the floors and walls being continuous. Changes in cross-section of the structure should be gradual if differential settlement of the structure is to be avoided. There should be a minimum of 50 mm cover to reinforcement adjacent to the water face, with normal cover recommendations being observed for other situations. The sequence and size of panel pours must be determined, as well as methods of 'curing' so that cracking from excessive shrinkage of the concrete is avoided.

28

The requirements of the concrete and the construction joints are considered in section 3.6 (b).

3.6 Waterproofed concrete

Concrete may be waterproofed by a number of methods, either during or after the original construction work. Work carried out after the concrete has been placed is generally in the form of either a surface skin or pore treatment. The *surface skin* may be asphalt tanking or a bituminous or p.v.a. painted membrane, and the *pore treatment* is either a material which when applied to the concrete surface acts as a gel which swells when in contact with the water, thus plugging the pores, or a material which lines the pores with a water-repelling agent, thereby preventing any capillary movement of moisture into the concrete.

The more common method of providing waterproof concrete is during construction, since subsequent additional work is eliminated. For concrete to be waterproof, the walls and slab should be at least 250 mm thick, with the concrete compacted to a dense uniform mass.

a) Additives and plasticisers The structure of hardened concrete contains a continuous network of capillary pores, and the proportion of these pores depends mainly on the water:cement ratio of the concrete and the effectiveness of the curing. If the water:cement ratio can be reduced without loss of strength or workability, the permeability of the concrete will be reduced, provided that compaction is achieved. A reduction in the water:cement ratio can be obtained by adding to the standard mix either ingredients which, by 'wetting' the aggregate surface, have the effect of reducing the volume of water required or ingredients which cause air-entrainment (very small air bubbles which act almost like ball-bearings and improve the workability). Alternatively, the pores may be filled or reduced in size by incorporating very fine inert materials such as chalk, gypsum, or p.f.a. into the mix.

b) Joints Construction joints are probably the weakest point in any waterproof structure and should be carefully detailed (fig. 3.10). Where tongues are used along a horizontal joint plane, the tongues should protrude upwards. The more common construction is to obtain a lightly roughened texture over the joint surface, with no laitance present. Immediately before the next pour, the joint surface should be thoroughly cleaned of debris and a thin layer of cement grout should be worked well into the surface.

Where high water pressures are expected and water-tightness is critical, the use of water-stops may be advisable. These form an additional barrier to the passage of moisture by being cast into the pour on each side of the joint plane. There are many shapes of water-stop, the more complex being extruded plastics, while other materials used are copper or stainless-steel strip and rubber. A continuous barrier must be maintained by welding the water-stops together where horizontal and vertical joints meet.

29

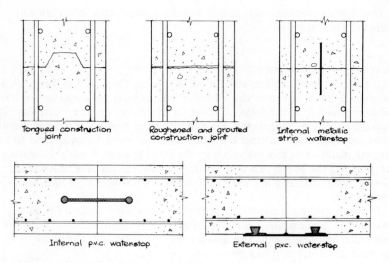

Fig. 3.10 Construction joints and water-stops

c) Quality control If good-quality concrete is to be produced, quality control is essential in both the batching and mixing of the aggregates and admixtures and in the pouring, compaction, and curing. The spacing of reinforcement should be such that the concrete can be adequately poured and compacted and at the same time permit access for joint preparation. On removal of formwork, the concrete surface should be inspected and any defects such as blow holes should be immediately rectified or made good.

3.7 Service entry
Because the majority of services are below ground, their entry into the building can create problems in the case of a basement. Not only must the service entry remain watertight, but also provision must be made for any relative movement between the building and the surrounding ground.

In waterproof-concrete basements, a pipe would normally have a puddle flange welded on (fig. 3.11), and this would be located centrally in the wall thickness. In the case of tanking, additional sleeving is provided around the pipes, while cable services would be fed through a pipe and the remaining void subsequently be filled with a flexible waterproof sealant.

3.8 Safety precautions in excavation
The safety of operatives and surrounding structures is of paramount importance in any excavation work, and the Construction (General Provisions) Regulations 1961 lay down minimum requirements for such safety as follows.

30

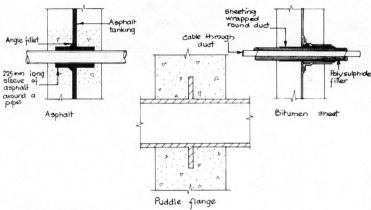

Fig. 3.11 Service entries

a) An adequate supply of suitable-quality timber or other material to prevent danger to people working in excavations over 2.1 m deep from material falling from the sides of the excavation.

b) The regular daily inspection of the excavation by a competent person and, before each shift where the depth exceeds 2 m, a signed record being kept on the prescribed form detailing the location, type, and state of excavation.

c) All the materials and work should be inspected, supervised, and carried out by competent persons. The work should be strong enough for its purpose, and all struts and braces should be adequately secured against accidental displacement.

d) If there is a forseeable danger of the excavation flooding, the employees must be able to reach places of safety.

e) No excavation should be carried out where there is a likelihood of temporary or permanent structures collapsing.

f) Excavations should be fenced off if their depth exceeds 2.0 m, except for access of personnel, machines, or materials, or where it is or has been impractical to do so.

g) Materials should not be stacked near the edge of the excavation nor plant be moved in the vicinity if there is a likelihood of the sides of the excavation collapsing.

Methods of protecting the excavation are shown in fig. 3.12. It is also essential that the site is generally tidy and that protective clothing and equipment are used.

3.9 Selection of fill material
There are a number of factors which will determine the materials used for filling and levelling on a given site, as follows.

31

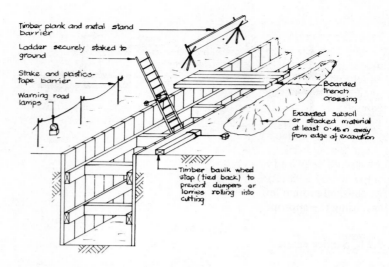

Timber plank and metal stand barrier

Ladder securely staked to ground

Stake and plastics-tape barrier

Warning road lamps

Boarded trench crossing

Excavated subsoil or stacked material at least 0·45 m away from edge of excavation

Timber baulk wheel stop (tied back) to prevent dumpers or lorries rolling into cutting

Fig. 3.12 Methods of protecting excavation

a) *Purpose of filling* The purpose for which filling is required will determine the range of suitable materials, e.g. a wide range of materials with
no specific strength requirement could be used for landscaping, while
the sub-base filling to a road (see chapter 25) must attain a suitable
strength.

b) *Angle of repose* This is particularly important in embankments, since
the amount of land occupied can be reduced by a fill having a larger
angle of repose. Similarly, the larger the angle of repose the less stress
is imposed on a retaining wall.

c) *Cost and availability* The cost of imported material and its availability
are frequently deciding factors in material selection. On road construction it may be cheaper to import fill material and pay for the tipping of
excess excavation nearby, rather than haul excavated materials over long
distances for use as filling.

d) *Ease of handling* Some materials are easier to handle and compact than
others, and this may also have an effect on the cost of the operation.

e) *Strength and compaction* The ability of a material to attain suitable
strength with minimum compaction is an important design consideration
where filling is required for structural purposes, particularly where subsequent settlement is to be avoided.

f) *Drainage* Where low moisture content is important, such as behind
retaining walls, the ability of the material to permit free drainage must
be considered.

Suitable materials for bulk filling include p.f.a.; crushed rock; sands; gravels;
cohesive soils; and soil which is not perishable (e.g. peat is unsuitable), frozen,
or subject to spontaneous combustion.

32

3.10 Backfilling to retaining walls

The backfilling to retaining walls usually consists of the replacing of subsoil excavated during the construction operation. However, the compaction of such material, usually by mechanical means, is likely to induce stresses in the wall which the wall must be able to withstand.

Filling around the base of the wall, at the heel and toe, may be carried out immediately, but the filling around the stem should not be done until the wall has reached its design strength. To reduce the problems of ground-water pressure, suitable drainage material is carefully placed against the back of the wall (hand-placed brick rubble is ideal for this purpose). The remainder of the backfill should be placed in layers approximately 200 to 300 mm deep and be compacted by a vibrating roller.

The finished ground level is obtained by a final covering of topsoil or pavings, using the appropriate construction.

3.11 Topsoil

Topsoil, being a valuable commodity, is stripped from the site before excavation work proceeds and is stockpiled on the site for subsequent reuse. On completion of the works it should be replaced to a minimum depth of 100 mm. If it is to be suitable for sustaining plant life, the topsoil should contain an adequate amount of humus, be friable, not contain weeds, and have all stones and hard material in excess of 40 mm diameter removed. These latter requirements can be achieved in the spreading and levelling operation by the use of suitable rakes.

3.12 Use of imported fill

Imported fill is used in any situation where the excavated material is unsuitable for the purpose. Its main use is in the making up of levels to provide a suitable formation. Many specifications call for a weak concrete fill in situations where a contractor has over-excavated the formation, thereby ensuring a material at least as dense as the original subsoil.

The most important consideration in using imported fill is the achievement of good compaction, thereby reducing the problems of any long-term settlement. On small-scale operations this compaction is achieved by the following.

a) *Vibrating-plate tamp* — consisting of a steel plate attached to a vibrating unit; manually operated.

b) *Trench compactor* — a vertical cylindrical power unit operating a piston which bears down on a spring-loaded steel plate; manually operated.

c) *Vibrating roller* — a self-propelled steel roller with a vibrating unit; may be a manually guided single roller or driver-operated with two rollers. A larger single roller with vibrator unit may be towed by a tractor to consolidate large areas of granular material.

Other items of compaction plant for larger sites include

d) *Pneumatic-tyred rollers* The wheels are mounted in separate independently sprung axles in such a way that the tread pattern of the rear wheels fills in the gaps left by the front wheels (fig. 3.13). The compaction is achieved

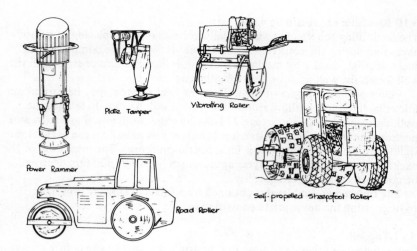

Fig. 3.13 Compaction equipment

by the kneading action of the tyre pressure provided by the ballasted weight of the machine. The roller may be either towed or self-propelled.

e) *Sheepsfoot roller* The rollers of the machine consist of a number of rows of steel projections mounted on a steel cylinder. The projections may be either tapered (for coarse granular material) or club-footed (for cohesive material). These rollers may be towed or self-propelled, and their effectiveness is dependent on the speed of travel over the surface.

In all cases the most effective consolidation of fill material is obtained by compacting thin (200 to 300 mm) layers rather than thick layers, since even the vibrating compaction methods have their effectiveness reduced by increase in depth.

4 Piling

Understands the materials and techniques used in sheet piling.

4.1 *Defines sheet piling.*
4.2 *Describes circumstances in which sheet piles are used.*
4.3 *Sketches and describes the construction and methods of driving sheet piling.*
4.4 *Describes methods of extracting sheet piles.*

Understands the reasons for the types of piles available and the installation techniques for bearing piles.

4.5 *Defines piled foundations.*
4.6 *States conditions under which piled foundations would be used for structures up to four storeys high.*
4.7 *Sketches and describes the construction and installation of*
    a) prefabricated driven piles,
    b) driven in-situ piles,
    c) bored piles.

Acknowledgement is due to the Technician Education Council for permission to use the content of the TEC units in this chapter. The council reserves the right to amend the content of its units at any time.

4.1 Sheet piling

Sheet piling may be defined as the construction of a wall of sheet piles which are driven vertically into the ground to exclude earth or water from an excavation. The wall may be supported by strutting across the width of an excavation, by single-sided raking support, single-sided cantilever support, or propped cantilever support (fig. 4.1).

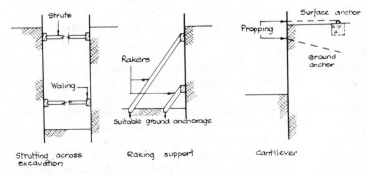

Fig. 4.1   Methods of sheet-pile support

35

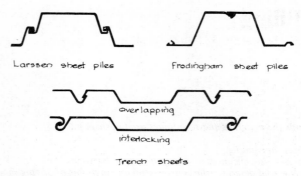

Fig. 4.2 Sheet-pile sections

Sheet piles are normally formed of steel, but precast concrete and timber may also be used. Steel-sheet piles are manufactured with flat or profiled sections of various lengths, with an overlapping or interlocking joint (fig. 4.2), and have the advantage of a high strength-to-weight ratio.

4.2 Usage of sheet piles

Sheet piling can be expensive in terms of driving and extraction, but has a number of advantages:

a) interlocking joints provide a reasonably watertight joint for use in water-logged ground or open water;
b) the piles can be driven before any excavation work begins, thereby improving safety;
c) piles may be driven into an impermeable stratum below a permeable one, thus cutting off the flow of ground water in the area;
d) the amount of bracing may be reduced in comparison to that required for timbering.

Lightweight trench sheeting is suitable for supporting excavations in most types of soil up to a depth of 5 m. Deeper excavations will require a heavier-section sheet, preferably with interlocking joints. This form of sheeting is the most widely used and is suitable for both temporary and permanent works in areas such as retaining walls, quays and harbour works, river banks, sea-defence works, bridge piers, and general deep-foundation works.

4.3 Driving sheet piles

Sheet piling is constructed by driving into the ground a series of sheets which either interlock or overlap by a required distance.

a) Guides There are two commonly used methods of guiding the sheets during driving: (i) using a trestle framework, (ii) in panels.

i) *Trestle framework* This consists of trestles which support walings. The framework, being of large-section timber or steelwork, is free-standing but, being heavy, requires moving and positioning by crane. The heavy sections are required to resist any tendency for the sheets to lean during

36

driving. The framework is positioned and the pile is inserted between the walings. To ensure accurate sheet location, timber spacer blocks are positioned between the pile and the waling before driving begins (fig. 4.3(a)).

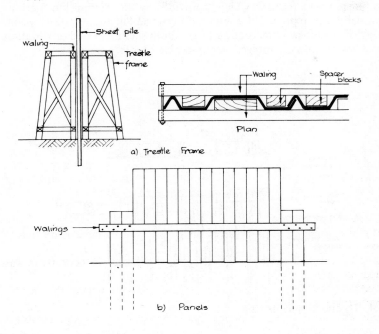

Fig. 4.3 Guides for sheet piles

ii) *Driving in panels* In this case two pairs of sheets are pitched and are carefully driven to partial penetration at each end of a section of sheeting. Two steel or timber walings are then bolted to these sheets to provide the guide for the remaining sheets which make up the panel (12 to 24 sheets). The end pairs remain partially driven in order to provide a support for adjacent panels, after which the panel itself provides the guide for the final driving of these sheets, fig. 4.3(b).

b) Driving equipment There are three categories of driving equipment:

i) *Percussion* A hammer is dropped on to a dolly or anvil block located on the top of the sheet pile, the drop hammer being activated by either steam, compressed air, or diesel. The driving rig is supported from a crane during the whole driving operation.

ii) *Vibratory* The vibration, induced in the driver, is transmitted through the sheet pile and causes a redistribution of soil particles which allows the weight of the driver to force the sheet into the ground. This operation is rather noisy and should be sound-proofed.

iii) *Hydraulic* In this case the piles are forced into the ground by hydraulic rams individually attached to eight sheet piles, forming a panel, the rams acting against a reaction which is provided by the ground skin friction on partially driven piles. This method ('Taywood Pilemaster', developed by Taylor Woodrow Construction Ltd) is both silent and free of vibration and has obvious advantages on city-centre sites (see fig. 4.4).

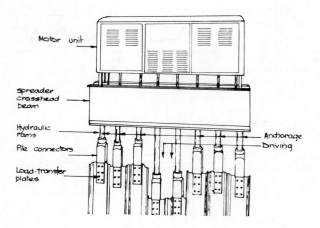

Fig. 4.4 Hydraulic pile driving

A variation of this method is to jack the sheets into the ground where there is suitable overhead reaction in the form of a bridge or, in the case of underpinning, a foundation (chapter 5).

4.4 Sheet-pile extraction

Holes are predrilled in the ends of the steel-sheet piles, and this not only allows for anchorage of the driving head but also facilitates the withdrawal of the sheets. An additional benefit is gained in both driving and removal of the sheets if the joints are well greased prior to driving. The case of withdrawal is also dependent upon the nature of the soil, the length of time the sheets have been in place, the depth of penetration into the ground, and the method of driving.

In order to avoid damage to the top of the pile, a special cap or extractor jaws should be used. Lightweight trench sheeting can frequently be extracted by the upward pull of a crane, but for the larger pile sections vibrators or an inverted double-acting hammer should be used in conjunction with a crane. Where the piles have been driven using the hydraulic system, their extraction can be effected by the same machine, with the rams working in the opposite direction.

4.5 Piled foundations

A piled foundation is one in which the foundation loading is transmitted through weak or unstable soil by means of columns to a lower stratum of suitable load-bearing capacity.

Piles may be classified in a number of ways, as follows.

a)   Piles which carry vertical loading are known as *bearing* piles, while those which restrain loads are known as *anchor* piles.

b)   The method by which the foundation loading is transferred to the subsoil by the pile may be categorised as end-bearing, friction, or a combination of the two methods. An *end-bearing* pile transfers the load through the subsoil to its base (similar to a column) which may be either bedrock or a dense stone or concrete bulb created to act in a similar manner to that of a pad foundation. A *friction* pile transfers the load to the surrounding subsoil by the adhesion or surface friction of that subsoil on the surface area of the pile.

c)   Forming the pile in the soil can be by either *displacement* or *replacement* methods. Displacement is where the soil is pushed aside as the pile is driven, while in replacement the soil is excavated and replaced by in-situ concrete.

4.6 Conditions for the use of piled foundations

Piled foundations are one of many alternative solutions for foundation-design problems. The selection of a piled foundation should be made primarily on the grounds of cost effectiveness and site expediency. Other considerations would be

a)   the depth at which suitable load-bearing strata are located in relation to a normal foundation depth;

b)   the founding of heavy point loads (e.g. from columns) which would cause a localised over-stressing of the soil;

c)   the presence of organic material in the subsoil, such as peat;

d)   the effect on adjacent properties of foundation loading at normal depths;

e)   the swelling and shrinkage of clay subsoils as a result of seasonal moisture movements;

f)   the presence of a high water table which would cause problems in the construction of the more traditional foundations;

g)   the differential settlement across a site caused by changes in strata or building on poorly consolidated fill materials;

h)   the anchorage of cantilever structures or other frames likely to cause negative foundation pressures;

j)   the 'pinning together' of various levels of inclined strata which would otherwise slip as a result of additional loading.

In most circumstances the above considerations must be taken into account whether the project is one of four storeys or twenty storeys.

4.7 Pile construction

a) Prefabricated driven piles   The materials used are (i) timber, (ii) steel, (iii) concrete.
  i) *Timber piles* – generally used for coastal works or in areas of the world where timber is readily available. The piles are of 300 to 500 mm square cross-section, in lengths varying from 15 to 24 m, and are made from Douglas fir, pitch pine, or hardwoods such as greenheart. In order to prevent the pile being damaged during driving, a steel ring or band is fitted to the head and a cast-iron or mild-steel shoe is fitted to the toe where hard ground is likely to be encountered (fig. 4.5). The piles should be cut off below the lowest anticipated water level and be capped with reinforced concrete, so that any possibility of rot from fluctuating moisture content is avoided.

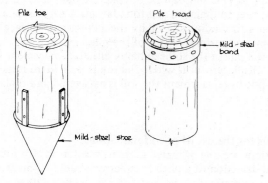

Fig. 4.5   Timber-pile details

  ii) *Steel piles* (fig. 4.6)   There are four main categories of steel pile. The H-section (or universal steel beam) is suitable for high axial loading and driving in hard ground. The box pile, which is made up of a number of standard steel sheets welded together, may be driven with an open or closed toe, the pile giving good resistance in soft subsoil. The tube pile is

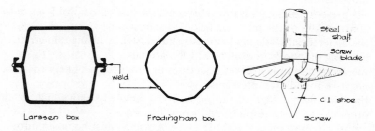

Fig. 4.6   Steel-pile details

40

similar to the box pile in its action but is formed by welding a steel plate into a continuous helix having a diameter which can vary from 250 to 600 mm. The screw pile consists of a solid or hollow steel shaft with a cast-iron helical blade of some 600 mm to 3.0 m diameter at the toe, which is screwed into the ground by applying a torque to the upper end of the shaft.

iii) *Precast concrete piles* The most common cross-section is the square, although polygonal and circular sections are also used. The concrete may be either prestressed or normally reinforced, but in addition to the strength requirement for working conditions the pile must also be designed to resist the handling and driving stresses (fig. 4.7).

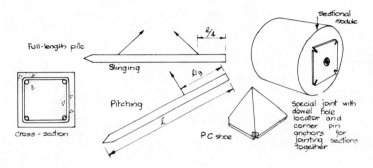

Fig. 4.7 Precast-concrete-pile details

The information on subsoil conditions must be accurate as possible where these piles are being used since, although they may be shortened without too much difficulty, they are very difficult to extend satisfactorily. In order to overcome this problem, the *composite* pile was developed, consisting of a series of precast concrete shells and a shoe, forming the outer casing of the pile, threaded over a steel mandrel, the whole assembly being driven into the ground using a drop hammer. The pile may be lengthened by the addition of further shells until the required depth or set is reached, after which the mandrel is removed and the shell is filled with in-situ concrete, reinforced as required, fig. 4.8.

The equipment used to drive preformed piles (fig. 4.9) consists of either a pile frame or crane and leader, a hammer, and a driving head or helmet. The leader is used to guide the pile during its initial penetration as well as providing a slide within which the hammer can operate. The hammer action is similar to the alternatives described in section 4.3(b)(i), the weight and drop being determined by the pile type and the ground conditions (a heavy hammer dropped a short distance being more effective than a light hammer dropping a long distance). The driving head is used to transmit the impact forces to the pile without damaging the pile head. With precast concrete piles a hardwood dolly is inserted to cushion the hammer blow on the helmet.

41

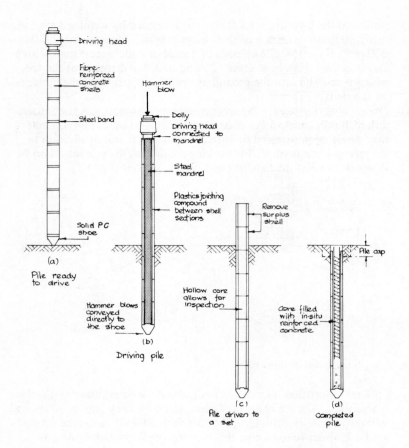

Fig. 4.8 Shell piles

In order to ensure the load-carrying abilities of a pile, it is generally driven to a 'set'. This means that the pile must be driven until such time as the penetration under a specified number of standard blows of the hammer is equal to or less than that predetermined by the designer.

b) Driven in-situ piles (fig. 4.10) The difference between a driven pile and a bored pile is that the driven pile displaces the subsoil whereas the subsoil is removed in the case of the bored pile.

A steel pile tube is pitched in on the ground at the pile position, using either a crane and leader in the case of a long pile tube or a set of shear legs in the case of short extendable tubing. A charge of suitable aggregate is placed in the tube and is consolidated into a solid plug by a drop hammer operating within the tube. Further blows of the hammer on the plug drive both plug

42

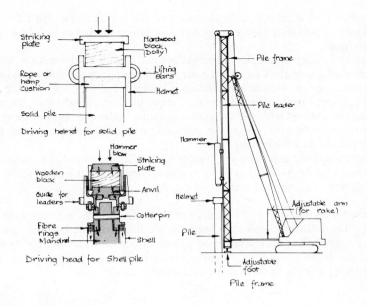

Fig. 4.9 Pile-driving equipment

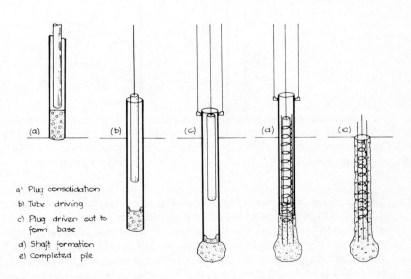

a) Plug consolidation
b) Tube driving
c) Plug driven out to form base
d) Shaft formation
e) Completed pile

Fig. 4.10 Driven in-situ piling

and tube into the subsoil, until the required depth is attained. The tube is then anchored, and further blows of the hammer force the plug out of the bottom of the tube.

Charges of dry or semi-dry concrete are placed in the tube and rammed into the subsoil at the base of the tube, forming an enlarged bulbous base. A reinforcing cage with helical binding is lowered into the tube, and the pile shaft is formed by pouring additional charges of concrete into the tube and consolidating them with the hammer (operating inside the cage) while at the same time slowly withdrawing the tube, care being taken to ensure that there is always concrete within the tube.

The completed pile has a very rough shaft resulting from the consolidation of the surrounding subsoil as the concrete is compacted, thereby providing a high degree of frictional bearing.

c) Bored piles (fig. 4.11) These are similar to driven piles in that a steel lining tube is taken down to the required depth and the method of constructing the pile then follows the same pattern as described in (b) above. The essential difference is the removal of the subsoil from the lining tube. This removal is achieved by the use of (i) a *coring tool* or (ii) an *auger.*

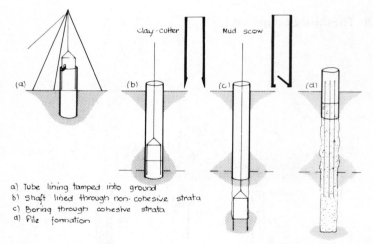

a) Tube lining tamped into ground
b) Shaft lined through non-cohesive strata
c) Boring through cohesive strata
d) Pile formation

Fig. 4.11 Bored piling

i) Using a tripod hoist powered by a diesel or compressed-air winch, a 1.5 m length of tube (400 to 600 mm diameter) is positioned on the ground in the pile position and is tamped into the ground using the weight of the coring tool. The material inside the tube is removed by raising and dropping the coring tool within the tube until the coring tool is full and then discharging the excavated material at ground level to one side of the tube. A second length of tube is screwed to the first and

44

tamped down, and further excavation is carried out. This procedure is repeated until the required depth is attained.

The type of coring tool will depend upon the type of subsoil, the two main types being the clay-cutter for cohesive soils and the mud scow, which has a flap valve, for non-cohesive soils.

The method of construction is particularly useful in areas where there is restricted headroom or for underpinning works (see chapter 5).

ii) The auger, mounted on a crane, drills a hole at the pile position, either to the full depth or to part depth depending on soil conditions. The excavated material is brought to the surface on the auger blades and is ejected by rapid reverse rotation of the blades. A steel lining tube is inserted and driven, by percussive methods, to provide temporary support to the borehole, during both further drilling and subsequent concrete placement.

The increased loadings of both buildings and their contents have increased the load-carrying requirements of piles. Large-diameter piles (in excess of 600 mm diameter) are being used with increasing regularity, their load-carrying capacity being further improved by the increase in their base size. This is achieved by using a suitable size of auger to excavate the shaft while a special under-reaming tool excavates an enlarged base (fig. 4.12).

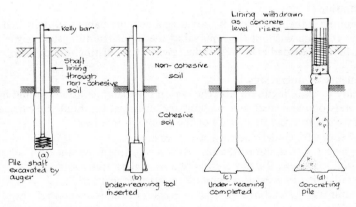

Fig. 4.12 Large-diameter under-reamed piles

45

5 Underpinning and dewatering

Understands the principles, techniques, and procedures involved in underpinning and dewatering.

**5.1 Defines underpinning.*
**5.2 Sketches and describes the underpinning operation to lower the existing strip foundation supporting a wall.*
**5.3 Lists the precautions necessary to prevent damage to the existing structure.*
5.4 Describes the reasons for dewatering subsoil.*
5.5 Lists the information required before beginning dewatering operations.*
5.6 Describes the 'pumping from sumps' method of dewatering.*
**5.7 Describes the installation of land drains.*

Acknowledgement is due to the Technician Education Council for permission to use the content of the TEC units in this chapter. The council reserves the right to amend the contents of its units at any time.

5.1 Definition

Underpinning is the operation of providing a new permanent support beneath walls and columns without the removal of the superstructure, such new support being provided at or below the level of the existing foundation.

5.2 Sequence of operations

Before any work is begun on site, the reason for such operations should be fully understood and sufficient preliminary investigation should be carried out to provide an accurate picture of the problems involved.

The reasons for underpinning a structure are

a) to prevent settlement of the foundation resulting from uneven loading, subsoil weakness, the dewatering of a subsoil by tree roots, or the degradation of an existing foundation by chemical action;

b) to improve the load-bearing characteristics of the wall foundations, which in turn will permit extensions to the existing superstructure or changes of use;

c) to allow the adjacent ground or floor levels to be lowered.

The investigate work would include

i) reasons for a settlement;

ii) a soil investigation to determine chemical content and depths of suitable load-bearing subsoil;

iii) a detailed survey of the existing building, including all defects and structural weaknesses.

The preliminary work would include

iv) the serving of notices on the owners of adjoining properties as to the nature and extent of the work;

v) the obtaining of local-authority approvals for the proposed works;

vi) the obtaining of permissions from adjoining property owners to carry out temporary works both on and in such properties so as to prevent nuisance or damage to such properties.

The lowering of an existing strip foundation is carried out in sections or bays, the length of which should generally not exceed 1.5 m or a quarter of the total wall length, whichever is the smaller.

A bay approximately 1.0 m wide is excavated alongside the existing wall to the depth required for the new foundation, the excavation exposing the existing foundation and also being carried out under it. The new foundation is cast with dowel bars projecting longitudinally from each end to provide foundation continuity when the adjacent bay is cast. Brickwork is constructed up to the underside of the existing foundation, with a weak concrete backfill being poured into the void created on the inaccessible side of the work. The brickwork is generally of good quality, consisting of class-B engineering bricks with 1:3 cement mortar, the ends of the wall length being toothed to provide subsequent continuity. The final pinning between the new wall and the soffit of the existing foundation is carried out by ramming a 1:3 semi-dry mix of rapid-hardening cement and 10 mm down graded aggregate into the void. The final operation is the removal of the projection of the existing foundation, thus preventing any load transference from the existing foundation to the backfilling of the completed bay, see fig. 5.1.

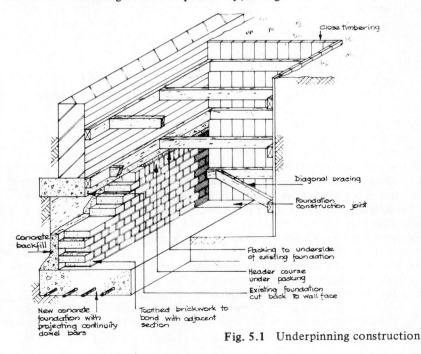

Fig. 5.1 Underpinning construction

The sequence of operations is repeated in each bay until the whole work is completed. It should be noted that there is a sequence for constructing the various bays (see fig. 5.2) so that no two adjacent bays are constructed consecutively.

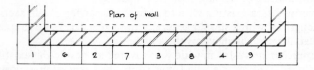

Fig. 5.2 Underpinning sequence

5.3 Safety precautions
In order to prevent damage to the existing structure as a result of the underpinning operation, a number of safety measures may be taken either severally or individually, depending on the condition of the structure:
a) *Window bracing* (fig. 5.3) This is provided in order to maintain the structural opening in the same alignment during the work.

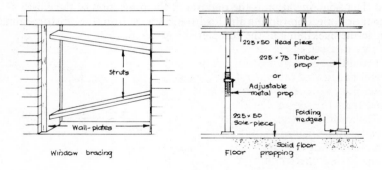

Fig. 5.3 Window bracing and floor propping

b) *Floor propping* This not only maintains constant floor-to-ceiling heights but may also have the effect of relieving a certain amount of load from the wall, providing a suitable temporary foundation is provided (e.g. a solid floor).
c) *Needling* (see chapter 7) removes a certain proportion of the wall loading from the existing foundation.
d) *Shoring* (see chapter 7) not only removes some of the load from the wall but also provides temporary stability to the wall.
e) The excavation should be provided with *close timbering* (see volume 2, section 4.4), not only to provide safe working conditions for the work force but also to prevent any subsidence of the ground which would affect the wall in question.

5.4 Reasons for dewatering

The reasons for the dewatering of a soil are

a) to allow excavation and other work below the water table to be carried
    out in drier conditions, thereby allowing economical working of both
    men and machines and improved quality control of materials;
b) to improve the angle of repose of the soil surrounding an excavation,
    thereby allowing steeper batters, less temporary ground support, and
    improved general working conditions;
c) to reduce the ground-water pressure, either temporarily or permanently,
    thereby reducing the cost of temporary or permanent ground-retaining
    structures such as timbering, sheet piling, or retaining walls;
d) temporarily to improve the load-bearing capacity of the soil, thereby
    improving the working conditions for both the labour force and vehicles;
e) permanently to improve the load-bearing capacity of the soil, thus
    enabling a more economic foundation to be designed.

5.5 Information for dewatering

The information required before beginning the dewatering of a site is

a) the standing level of the water table, together with any seasonal
    variations;
b) the nature of the strata down to and including the draw-off level;
c) the permeability of the strata between water-table level and draw-off
    level;
d) the rate and direction of flow of ground water in the subsoil.

From the above information, an anticipated draw-down curve may be
established, giving the water-table level in the ground surrounding the proposed site so that the effects on adjacent land and properties of removing
water from the subsoil can be estimated (fig. 5.4).

The information will also enable the soils engineer to forecast the volume
of water to be removed, so that suitable pumps may be used, the suitability
of a pump being determined by the pumping rate, the height of suction or
discharge, and the pump size.

Where large volumes of water have to be removed from the ground, information will be required about accessible water courses, land drains, or
surface-water drains into which such water may be discharged, and the likely
effect of such discharges.

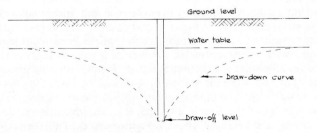

Fig. 5.4 Ground-water draw-down curve

5.6 Pumping from sumps

This is the most commonly used method of dewatering, since it can be applied in the majority of ground conditions. The method, involving a small sump hole cut below the level of the formation from which accumulated water is pumped, has been described in volume 2, section 4.7.

There are two major problems in pumping from sumps: (a) ground movement and (b) pumping height.

a) *Ground movement* occurs as a result of fine soil particles being washed along by the flow of water towards the sump. This is likely to cause a collapse of the embankment or, worse still, of any timbering as a result of the regrading of soil which can occur resulting from the loss of the fine soil particles. Also, the removal of the fine particles may increase the flow of water through certain soil types, with further adverse effects.

b) *The pumping height* is purely dependent on the depth of the sump below the discharge point. Since the majority of excavations are less than 7 m deep, a suction-type pump will be suitable, the normal maximum suction lift being some 7.5 to 8.0 m. If the depth exceeds 7 m then either a two-stage pumping operation must be employed (fig. 5.5) or a submersible pump must be used, the latter being able to lift the water by centrifugal force to a height of some 16 m.

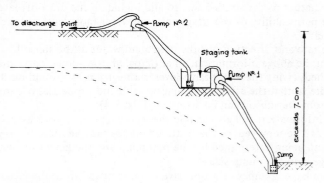

Fig. 5.5 Two-stage pumping

5.7 Land drains

Subsoil or land drainage has already been defined and briefly described in volume 2, section 22.4. The laying of a land drain is very similar to that adopted for surface-water or foul drainage in that the invert should be to even falls and, with the exception of the natural layout pattern, in straight lines. Modern techniques use the mole plough in conjunction with laser beams which control not only the direction of the plough but also the depth of the mole, thus ensuring an even pipe gradient irrespective of the surface contours.

Where the drain is being laid in a trench, it is not advisable to provide a granular bedding, since this will provide a waterway as in a French-drain system.

In order to prevent silting of the land drain, porous pipes or pipes having only the lower half of their surface perforated should be used, especially if they can be jointed together rather than using open or butt joints.

The connections between main and branch drains may be made using ordinary drainage fittings; alternatively, butt joints may.be used, with the crowns of the pipes rather than the inverts being level.

The major problem in land drainage is the silting up of the system, and in order to prevent silt clogging up the drain it is essential that suitable backfill materials are used (fig. 5.6) so that fine material is filtered out of the water before it enters the system. Silt will, however, inevitably enter the system as a result of root action or external physical or mechanical damage. It should, therefore, be prevented from causing damage at the outfall or discharge point by the incorporation into the scheme of either a mud gulley, an intercepting trap, or a lined soakaway with an access facility.

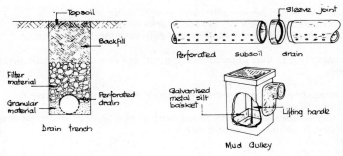

Fig. 5.6 Land drainage

6   Concrete work

Understands the use of concreting plant.

6.1 Identifies the economic and other factors affecting the choice of concreting plant.
**6.2 Defines quality control.*
**6.3 Selects the methods of storage of materials and the mixing of materials applied to quality control of concrete.*
  6.4 Identifies the common types of plant used for the production, transporting, and placing of concrete.*
**6.5 Lists the reasons for the controlled curing of concrete.*
**6.6 Explains how concrete can be satisfactorily cured by means of sprayed water, hessian and straw blankets, and polythene sheeting.*

Understand the principles of prestressed concrete and its structural application to buildings.

6.7 Distinguishes between prestressed concrete and reinforced concrete as structural concrete.
6.8 Compares the merits of prestressed concrete with those of other structural materials with particular reference to
  a) quality,
  b) size and dimension,
  c) weight,
  d) fire resistance,
  e) resistance to corrosion,
  f) water resistance,
  g) economy.

Acknowledgement is due to the Technician Education Council for permission to use the content of the TEC units in this chapter. The council reserves the right to amend the content of its units at any time.

6.1 Choice of concreting plant

There a number of factors which affect any choice of concreting plant for any given site, and these in turn are affected by the contractor's attitude to plant in general.

a)   Probably the most important aspect is *financial*, which may be broken down into four components, as follows.
  i)   Hire or buy? If plant is being hired the contractor can usually get the exact item(s) he requires, whereas it is seldom the case when buying that the cost of a piece of equipment is written off against one job, therefore compromises are made in respect of suitability for a particular site. At the same time, cash flow and investment also play a part in the decision.

ii) Running cost. The expenses not only of fuel but of the auxiliary men and equipment to operate the various machines.

iii) The maintenance costs in terms of servicing, spares, and site costs resulting from down-time.

iv) How much does the concrete cost to produce?

b) The *size or capacity of the mixer* output must be matched with either (i) the maximum anticipated daily or hourly demand or (ii) an average or normally anticipated demand.

In case (i) the mixer will be working to capacity for only some 10% of its time on site; in case (ii) the mixer will be fully used for some 60% of its time on site, with the periods in which demand exceeds production being catered for by the purchasing of ready-mixed concrete.

c) *Planning* may indicate that the use of two smaller mixers operating on different areas of the site would be more practical than one large central batching plant.

d) The *method of loading and discharging* the mixer should be considered, together with the duration of the mixing cycle.

e) The *method and duration of mixing* has an effect on the quality of the concrete produced, and this quality may be critical at certain stages of the work.

f) The *availability of space* on site for a batching plant can also dictate the choice, particularly in respect of site-mixed or ready-mixed concrete.

g) The ease of *transporting a mixer* or batching plant from one site to another may be high on the list of priorities of a small builder.

h) The *type of plant* that a contractor already has or intends to use on a site for the movement of the concrete once mixed (e.g. dumper, crane, etc.) may dictate a particular type of batching plant.

j) *Standardisation of equipment* in terms of one plant manufacturer immediately imposes certain restrictions of choice.

6.2 Quality control

This is the operation of ensuring that the concrete in its finished and complete state is at least up to the minimum standards laid down by either the client, or the contractor (for his own sake), or the various legislative requirements.

The operations involved are the quality standards and the testing where applicable of

a) materials — water, cement, aggregates, admixtures;

b) materials storage — moisture content, cleanliness;

c) batching — mix design, masses or volumes;

d) mixing — thoroughness, cleanliness, workability, strength;

e) transporting — segregation, loss of grout;

f) placing — methods, workmanship;

g) formwork — accuracy, alignment, strength, joint tightness;

h) reinforcement — cleanliness, location, size;

j) compaction — vibration, density;

k) curing — temperature, loss of moisture;

l)   completed concrete — appearance, strength.
It is only by constant and rigorous checking of these items that quality standards can be achieved and maintained.

6.3 Storage and mixing

The method of storing the materials used in producing concrete can have a direct bearing on the concrete quality.

Cement which has not been stored in dry conditions or has been in store for a long time may exhibit the phenomenon of 'air setting' — the formation of lumps of hydrated cement. Unless these lumps are removed, the strength of the finished concrete will be adversely affected. This may be avoided by the use of silos which ensure a good protection from weather and a 'first in first out' usage.

The aggregate stores should be self-draining and located so as not to become contaminated with other materials. It is preferable for these stores to be as large as possible, so that uniformity of aggregate grading and moisture content is achieved. Variation in moisture of the aggregate will affect the water:cement ratio and hence the concrete workability and strength; these two latter items are also affected by changes in the aggregate grading. At the same time, the aggregates should not be affected by frost, which may require either the provision of covers or the incorporation of steam heaters, since ice will affect not only setting times but also the density of the mix.

Thorough mixing of the constituents is essential if a uniform mix is to be achieved. The water should enter the mixer at the same time as the other constituents, and there should be no loss of cement. Mixing of the constituents, other than the water, can be partially achieved by the correct loading sequence into mass-batching equipment where fitted.

Cement, in the form of grout, may be lost in the first batch of a day by the material coating the drum interior and the paddles or blades; in this case the aggregate proportion should be reduced. The mixer should be cleaned thoroughly and washed out at the end of a day's work to remove this coating, as well as on occasions where the type of cement is changed or after stoppages during which time the coating could have developed a set.

6.4 Types of plant

a) Mixers   There are four main types of concrete mixer (fig. 6.1), designated by a letter or letters:

(T) tilting drum — a conical drum with one opening; rotates on a movable axis.

(NT) non-tilting drum — a cylindrical drum with openings at each end, rotating on a horizontal axis. Discharge by means of a chute inserted into the drum.

(NTR) or (R) reversing drum — similar to (NT) but discharge by reversing the rotation of the drum.

(P) pan — a circular pan with discharge through a flap in the base of the pan. Either the pan rotates about a vertical axis with the blades fixed, or the pan is stationary while the blades rotate, or the pan and blades both rotate.

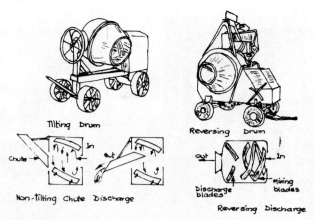

Fig. 6.1 Concrete mixers

Mixers are also classified by their capacity in litres for intake and output, e.g. a 300/200 mixer is one which will take 300 litres of material unmixed and produce from such a batch 200 litres of mixed concrete.

Mixers are generally powered by diesel or electric units, but the smaller mixers (90/75 to 240/175) may also be driven by petrol engines. Mobile mixers are in two forms: the dumper-mounted self-loading model and the lorry-mounted ready-mix delivery vehicle (see fig. 6.2).

Fig. 6.2 Mobile concrete mixers

b) Transport Concrete, which should generally be placed within half an hour of mixing, may be transported from the mixer to the point of placement in a number of ways, some specifically developed for concrete, others being multipurpose (fig. 6.3):

   i)   pump — hydraulic or mechanical ram; lorry-mounted or static
  ii) pump — compressed air
 iii) skip — hoisted by crane or fork-lift truck
 iv) conveyor belt
  v) monorail — powered or towed skips

Concrete-batching plant

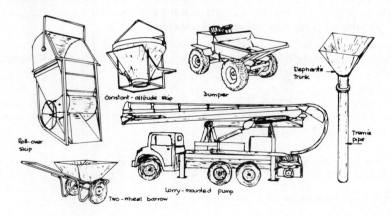

Roll-over skip

Constant-altitude skip

Dumper

Elephant's Trunk

Tremie pipe

Two-wheel barrow

Lorry-mounted pump

Fig. 6.3 Concrete transporters

vi)   jubilee rail — narrow-gauge railway
vii)   hoist
viii)   aerial ropeway
ix)   chute
x)   tremie pipe — long drops in trenches or liquids
xi)   single-wheel barrow

xii) double-wheel barrow (Dobbin barrow) — hand- or power-operated
xiii) three-wheel barrow
xiv) dumper
xv) lorry
xvi) ready-mix vehicles
xvii) mechanical/hydraulic excavator buckets — front or backactor

c) Placement The density and strength of a concrete is dependent to a large extent on the compaction once placed. Compaction methods include
  i) hand tamp — for slab areas;
  ii) vibrating-beam tamp — for slab areas;
  iii) poker (immersion) vibrator — driven mechanically or by compressed air and suitable for most situations;
  iv) formwork (external) vibrators — used where sections are very narrow or heavily reinforced, or generally where it would be impossible to use a poker vibrator. Formwork must be specially strengthened for this method.

6.5 Reasons for curing

Concrete requires the presence of water for the chemical reaction of hardening to take place. It is therefore essential that the water incorporated into the concrete at the mixing stage remains until full hydration has taken place. This hydration is accompanied by a generation of heat, which should be controlled: too low a temperature and the rate of hardening is slowed down; temperature below freezing point and the water will expand, causing permanent damage; too high a temperature within the concrete during the hardening period and thermal-contraction cracking will occur; too high a surface temperature and surface evaporation will occur, resulting in the concrete drying out and becoming weak and porous.

The operation of curing is designed to overcome all these problems so that the concrete becomes impermeable and durable, has good abrasion resistance, and has a dense hard surface which is free from cracks or crazing.

6.6 Methods of curing

Concrete contained within formwork will generally not require any curing, since the formwork provides a covering which will generally perform the curing requirements. It is the concrete which is open to the atmosphere which is at risk, e.g. the top of walls and columns or large floor slabs.

In order to prevent surface evaporation and overheating from the action of sun and wind, a number of methods have been developed as follows.
a) *Spraying* the concrete surface with water, thereby replacing any loss which may occur. Problems occur where surfaces are inclined or not perfectly smooth and horizontal.
b) *Hessian or straw* blankets spread over the concrete surface and suitably damped provide insulation as well as a moisture-holding medium
c) *Damp sand* provides similar protection to (b) above but without the same degree of insulation.

d) *Polythene sheeting* laid over but not on the concrete acts as a tent in which humidity can be maintained immediately the concrete is laid without having to wait until an initial set has developed.

e) *Spray coatings* form an impervious coating which may also act as a discolouring agent or a solar reflector. These membranes are generally unsuitable where further floor coatings are to be applied to the concrete surface (e.g. screeds).

Insulation against frost attack is provided by hessian or straw blankets, preferably dry, or polythene sheeting which will contain the heat generated by the chemical hydration process, thus counteracting the cold external conditions. Where severe conditions occur, the formwork could also be covered with hessian to provide additional insulation.

6.7 Prestressed concrete

Prestressing of concrete is the application of compressive forces to a concrete member before it is put into use within a structure. The location and magnitude of this stressing force can be chosen to obtain maximum design benefit under working conditions.

In ordinary reinforced-concrete members, the reinforcement is placed in the concrete with the main object being to carry the tensile stresses induced as a result of the loading condition (see section 9.6). Because of the weakness of concrete in tension and problems caused by cracking as a result of deflection, a structural member which is required to carry heavy loads must have a large cross-sectional area and also contain a large amount of reinforcement. This in turn increases the self-weight of a member and reduces the economic span.

The object of prestressing a concrete member is to eliminate the tensile forces — and any cracking — by cancelling their effects when the member is subjected to its working load. This is achieved by pre-compression (see fig. 6.4).

Pre-compression is achieved by either pre-tensioning or post-tensioning.

a) *Pre-tensioning* High-tensile-steel wires are stretched through the formwork prior to the precasting of a unit, and, when the concrete has been cast and allowed to gain sufficient strength, the stretching force on the wire is released. Because of their elasticity, the wires attempt to return to their original length, but the adhesion of the surrounding concrete prevents this, thus inducing compressive stresses into the unit. This process is often carried out by precast-concrete manufacturers at their factories.

b) *Post-tensioning* This is carried out on site. The members are generally cast in-situ, with ducts through which wire strands or threaded steel bars are subsequently inserted. When the concrete has matured, the strands or bars are stretched and anchored against special anchor blocks cast into the ends of the member, thus applying a compressive force at each end of the member. To prevent corrosion of the wires or tendons, the duct is finally filled with grout.

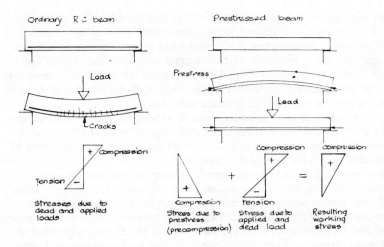

Fig. 6.4 Theory of prestressing

The location of the prestressing tendons within the depth of the unit is of critical importance, and it is therefore essential that the units are positioned the correct way up when being incorporated into the structure.

The design emphasis is now on the concrete and not the reinforcement, and it is essential that high-quality concrete, having good compressive strength, is used for prestressed work.

6.8 Comparison with other materials

a) *Quality* Because high-quality concrete and careful control of the stressing are essential, careful and expert supervision is required in every phase of the work, from material-quality control to erection. This is a disadvantage when compared with the other standard structural materials, e.g. reinforced concrete, steel, and timber. However, as the members act as a homogeneous material, the best qualities of both the steel and the concrete are obtained.

b) *Size* Because the material behaves homogeneously, depths of members for a given span are much less than those required for ordinary r.c. work. The effect of prestressing also reduces shear-stress problems, thereby permitting reduced web thicknesses in beams. The best shape for a prestressed-concrete beam is an 'I' similar to the steel UB (fig. 9.1). For long-span beams or bridges, prestressed concrete will generally provide the smallest cross-sectional dimensions.

c) *Weight* As a result of the reduction in size, the amount of concrete in a prestressed unit can be a third to a half that required for an r.c. unit, while the amount of steel used need only be a fifth to a tenth that required in normal reinforcement design. However, the span-to-weight ratio would still be higher than for equivalent steel or timber members.

59

d) *Fire resistance* British Standard Code of Practice CP 110 requires the cover to prestressing tendons to be approximately twice that required for ordinary reinforcement, and, since there is much more emphasis on concrete quality, particular attention must be paid to the type of aggregate used in respect of spalling. However, provided that the requirements of the code are met, no further fire protection of the member is required. This is not the case with structural steelwork.

e) *Corrosion* If the recommended cover is provided for the given location of a member and the tendons are completely surrounded by concrete, there should be no corrosion problems, whereas structural steel must be provided with a suitable protective coating.

f) *Water resistance* The requirement for high-grade concrete should immediately improve the water resistance of prestressed concrete, since a denser matrix will result, thereby reducing the pore sizes within the concrete. Water penetration through cracks resulting from tensile bending will also be eliminated, since the member will be under compression at all times. Prestressed concrete is therefore better than timber and ordinary reinforced concrete in resisting water, but marginally poorer than steel.

g) *Economy* Because of the high-quality requirements as well as the specialist stressing and anchorage equipment, prestressed-concrete members tend to be more expensive than members made of other materials. The exceptions to this are where (i) the work is of a very heavy load-bearing nature; (ii) the units can be produced in large numbers on a regular basis, as in the case of precast floors (chapter 13); or (iii) there are particular size restrictions imposed by the layout design of a structure.

7   Retaining walls and shoring

Understands the functions of retaining walls and the principles involved in their construction.

7.1   States the primary functions of retaining walls and factors affecting stability.
7.2   Sketches and describes typical retaining walls up to 5.0 m high.

Understands the principles of shoring.

*7.3   Sketches and explains the functions of dead, raking, and flying shore systems.
*7.4   Identifies the terminology of these systems and typical materials used.
*7.5   Describes the sequence of erecting and dismantling dead, raking, and flying shore assemblies.

Acknowledgement is due to the Technician Education Council for permission to use the content of the TEC units in this chapter. The council reserves the right to amend the content of its units at any time.

7.1 Functions and stability of retaining walls

The main functions of a retaining wall are safely to hold back or contain the materials, liquids, or wind which are placed or occur behind it.

Retaining walls hold back or contain their loads in one or a combination of the following ways:

> *self-weight or gravity*
> *anchorage*   } see fig. 7.1
> *shape*

and failure of the wall may occur as a result of the wall

> *fracturing*
> *overturning*
> *sliding*   } see fig. 7.1(c)
> *slipping or rotating*

The factors which affect the stability of a retaining wall are

a)   the angle of repose of the retained material, since it is the wedge of material above the angle-of-repose plane that the wall must retain;

b)   the resultant thrust on the wall from the material wedge, which in turn depends on the density of the material;

c)   the thrust of liquids or ground water — the effect of ground water may be reduced by incorporating suitable drainage in the form of weep holes and granular backfill;

d)   the thrust of any surcharge loading;

e)   the self-weight of the wall;

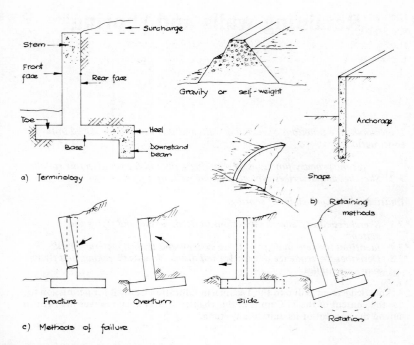

a) Terminology

b) Retaining methods

c) Methods of failure

Fig. 7.1 Retaining-wall terminology

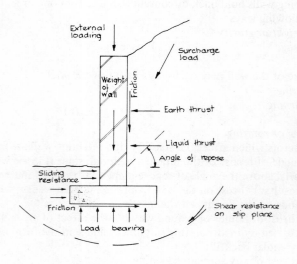

Fig. 7.2 Stability factors

f) the vertical loading from any structure located on top of the wall;
g) the friction between the retained material and the wall face;
h) the friction between the natural and artificial foundations;
j) the load-bearing characteristics of the natural foundation;
k) the resistance of the subsoil to the wall sliding;
l) the shear strength of the soil to prevent rotation.

The above factors are illustrated diagrammatically in fig. 7.2.

7.2 Typical retaining walls

There are various types of retaining wall, namely
a) mass,
b) cantilever,
c) counterfort,
d) diaphragm,
e) concrete crib.

a) *Mass* Constructed of masonry or concrete, these walls rely purely on their self-weight and base width for stability. They are generally not economic for heights exceeding 2.0 m, the base width being $\frac{1}{4}$ to $\frac{1}{3}$ of the height (fig. 7.3).

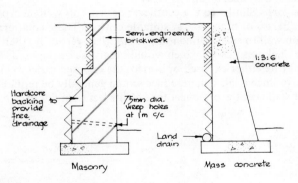

Fig. 7.3 Mass retaining walls

b) *Cantilever* Constructed of reinforced concrete, the walls may be cast in situ or formed using precast concrete sections. They make economic use of material and, as they weigh less than the mass wall, using the principle of levers for stability, are suitable for heights up to 7.0 m. There are three basic forms:
   i) with the base having a large heel whereby the weight of earth above is added to the weight of the wall for design purposes;
   ii) with the base having a large toe in order to reduce excavation and backfill cost;
   iii) a combination of (i) and (ii).

63

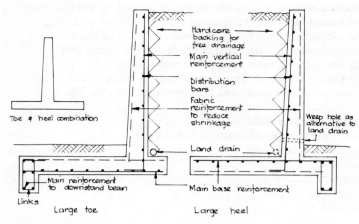

Fig. 7.4 Cantilever wall

In all cases the main reinforcement is placed in the tension face (the face in contact with earth), with nominal reinforcement in the other face to control shrinkage cracking. Additional resistance to sliding is provided by a downstand or heel beam (fig. 7.4).

c) *Counterfort* Similar to the cantilever design, this wall incorporates triangular beams or buttresses at suitable centres. These counterforts allow the main wall to span horizontally rather than vertically, thereby reducing the thickness of wall which would otherwise be required. The counterforts may be either exposed or buried, the exposed variety being more expensive since a fair concrete face would generally be required. This type of wall is not economical for heights less than 5.0 m.

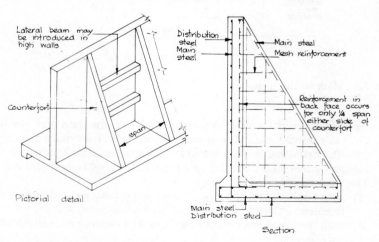

Fig. 7.5 Counterfort wall

64

d) *Diaphragm* (fig. 7.6)   Constructed to act as a pure cantilever, the wall is
created in one of two ways.
  i) A section of wall is excavated to its full depth and width by a grab
     or special drilling equipment, the excavated material being replaced
     by a thixotropic mud solution called Bentonite. This solution (fluid
     when activated) exerts a hydrostatic pressure on the sides of the
     excavation, thus eliminating the requirement for timbering. Reinforc-
     ing cages are placed through the Bentonite into the excavation, and
     concrete is poured through a tremie to form the wall. The displaced
     Bentonite, which does not affect either the bond between the con-
     crete and the reinforcement or the concrete strength, is collected for
     reuse on another section of the wall.

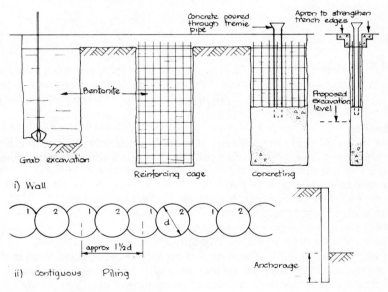

Fig. 7.6   Diaphragm wall

  ii) Bored piles are constructed to full depth along the line of the wall
      so that their centres are approximately one and a half times their
      diameter. While the concrete is still 'green', a further series of piles
      is bored between the first series so that an interlocking pile wall
      (contiguous piling) is created.
Once the wall is complete, the required excavation may proceed.
    This form of construction eliminates any earth-support requirements
during either construction or subsequent excavation, but, as in both cases
the concrete has been cast against the subsoil, a rough surface will be
exposed which will require subsequent facing — generally with gunnite.

e) *Concrete crib* These walls are basically a mass or gravity retaining wall and consist of a series of precast interlocking concrete units, forming a grillage pattern, which are infilled with soil or rock. They are generally set with a face batter of between 1:6 and 1:8, except where the height is less than the base width, in which case the wall is set vertically and is suitable for retaining embankments (fig. 7.7).

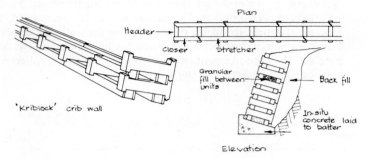

Fig. 7.7 Concrete-crib wall

SHORING

7.3 Shoring
Shoring is the provision of temporary support to a structure in order to prevent danger to people from possible collapse. It is provided in situations where a wall is unstable due to
a) subsidence, bulging, or leaning;
b) removal of supports during demolition or alteration works;
c) creation of new openings;
or where a new floor-support system is being created.
  There are three types of shores with different functions, as follows.
a) *Dead shores* (fig. 7.8)   These support both dead and imposed loads in the vertical direction only, and are used to relieve the loading either in an existing wall during the formation of an opening or in a floor during alteration work or the provision of new or additional support work. They must safely transmit, without movement, these loads to a lower level or a temporary foundation.
b) *Raking shores* (fig. 7.9)   These provide temporary support as well as stiffness to a wall which has already bulged or is likely to move as a result of structural alteration works. By virtue of the incline or rake, the shore is able to carry a certain amount of vertical loading as well as horizontal thrust. The angle of the rake is dictated by space availability around the structure, the lowest raker being set at about 45° to the horizontal.
c) *Flying shores* (fig. 7.10)   These provide horizontal restraint only, and are used where there is limited space available at ground level and there is a convenient wall against which to brace. Generally, flying shores are not used when the distance between walls exceeds 12.0 m.

66

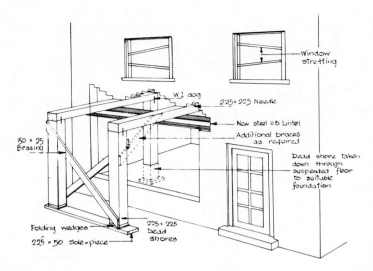

Fig. 7.8 Dead shoring

7.4 Shoring materials and terminology

Structural softwood is the most commonly used material in shoring, because of its adaptability and good strength-to-weight ratio. An alternative for large-scale operations is the use of scaffold tubing.

Since shoring provides structural support to a building, the sizes of the various members should be individually calculated but the sizes of members shown on the diagrams here are typical.

Terms commonly associated with shoring include the following.

Back shore	A support to a riding shore, resting on top of the top raker.
Brace	A member which holds the main structural member in position.
Binder	See 'brace'.
Cleat	A small timber member used to anchor and provide additional support for the needle.
Dog	A metal U-shaped spike used to anchor two butt-jointed structural members together.
Distance pieces	Spacing timbers between rakers at the base of a raking shore.
Folding wedges	A pair of wedges operating in opposite directions to tighten or slacken the shoring system.
Grillage	A base or platform of sleepers providing a foundation for the shore.
Needle	A timber or metal piece which is inserted into or through a wall and transfers load from the wall to the support system.

67

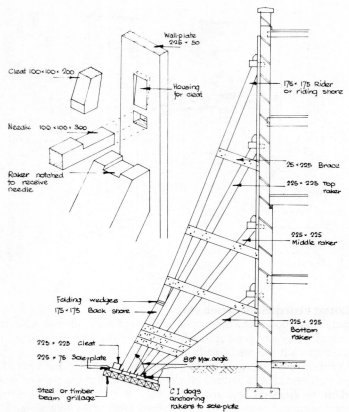

Fig. 7.9 Raking shoring

Raker (top, middle, bottom)	Inclined timber member(s) providing support in a raking shore.
Rider	The topmost raker, being supported by the back shore and not going down to ground level.
Shore legs	Vertical members supporting the needle in a dead shore.
Sole-plate	A load-spreading beam of timber or steel set on the floor, ground, or grillage.
Strainer or straining sill	A horizontal member providing support anchorage for the struts in a flying shore.
Strut	i) Inclined support members in a flying-shore system.
	ii) Members wedging wall-plates apart in window bracing.

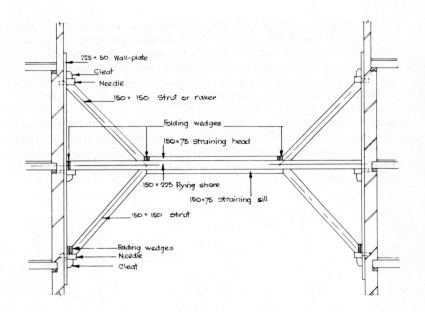

Fig. 7.10 Flying shoring.

Wall hook	A metal spike used initially to anchor a wall-plate to the wall.
Wall-plate or piece	A vertical or horizontal timber transferring some wall loads via the needle and cleat into the shore, or inside a window jamb.

7.5 Erection and dismantling of shoring

a) *Dead shore* When the number and position of shores required have been assessed from a thorough investigation, the weights of the floors, ceiling, and roof are relieved from the wall by propping between sole and head pieces using timber struts and folding wedges or adjustable steel props. This propping should be as close to the affected wall as possible, bearing in mind working-room requirements. Existing window openings should be strutted, removing the frames where necessary.

Holes are cut in the wall, floors, and ceilings to accommodate the shoring, and sole-plates and sleepers are positioned. The positioning of the needles will depend on the condition and weight of the wall, but they should generally be not more than 2.0 m apart. The needle is inserted through the wall, supported on the shore legs, and anchored to them by dogs. Packing is inserted as required between the needle and the wall, and the shoring is tightened up by the folding wedges. Bracing is finally added to stabilise the system.

69

On completion of the work and allowing a suitable time for the new work to attain sufficient strength, the folding wedges are gradually eased until the shore is free and the erection procedure is then reversed.

b) *Raking shores* After detailed investigation, holes are cut in the wall-plate to accommodate the needles in positions such that the centre line of the rakers will coincide with either the centre line of the bearing or the intersection of the floor and wall centre lines (see fig. 7.11). The wall-plate is offered to the wall and the wall is marked for the cutting of holes to receive the needles. When the wall-plate has been removed and these holes have been cut, the wall-plate is repositioned and anchored with wall hooks. The shore base is excavated and the grillage and sole-plate are positioned.

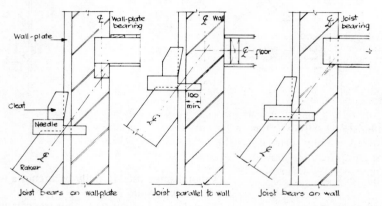

Fig. 7.11 Shore location

The rakers are cut and positioned against needles which are inserted through the wall-plate into the wall, beginning with the bottom rakes and working upwards. The raker is tightened into position by levering it down the sole-plate, which is set at an angle such that it is never at right angles to a raker (89° max.). The cleats, distance pieces, and dogs are positioned before the final bracing is fixed.

It should be remembered that the shoring is intended not to push a bulging wall back into position but to prevent further deterioration and to allow remedial works to be carried out. Dismantling is the reverse of the erection procedure.

c) *Flying shores* The sequence of erection and dismantling is similar to that described for raking shores, except that temporary support will be required for the flying shore until the struts have been positioned and tightened.

8   Scaffolding

Appreciates the principles of scaffolding, types, execution, and dismantling, with particular reference to safety requirements.

8.1 Identifies the principal reasons for the use of scaffolding systems.
8.2 Describes and compares independent, putlog, and mobile scaffold systems and ladders.
8.3 Identifies component parts of scaffold systems.

Acknowledgement is due to the Technician Education Council for permission to use the content of the TEC units in this chapter. The council reserves the right to amend the content of its units at any time.

8.1 Reasons for use

Scaffolding is a temporary framework erected to provide access and support for men and materials during construction, alteration, or maintenance works.

There are many forms of scaffold, ranging from the simple timber trestle to the complex tubular alloy framework used in large construction, and all are subject to the Construction (Working Place) Regulations 1966. These regulations require that the scaffold is strong enough to carry all loads, is stable, and that the platforms are safe to work on for the operatives and that materials do not fall off.

Scaffolding may also be used as a falsework to support formwork, to provide a barrier around excavations, or as a framework in shoring operations.

8.2 Scaffold types

a) Description
i) *Independent*   As the name implies, this form does not rely on the adjacent structure to provide support; however, it should be tied back to the structure at intervals in order to provide additional horizontal stability. It consists of two rows of vertical members called *standards* which are held in position by horizontal members — those running parallel to the building are termed *ledgers* and those at right angles are termed *transoms*. Stability of the framework is provided by longitudinal and transverse or wind bracing — see fig. 8.1. The scaffold boards which form the platform are supported on the transoms, while the workmen's safety is provided for by guard-rails and toe boards.

ii) *Putlog*   Similar to the independent type but having only one (outer) row of standards, the transoms (called *putlogs* in this case) being supported by the wall, fig. 8.2.

71

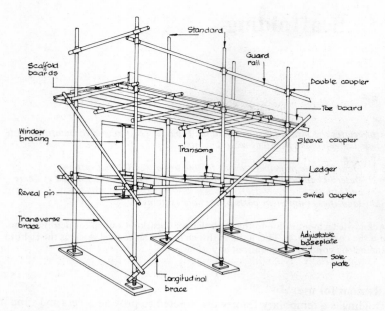

Fig. 8.1 Independent scaffolding

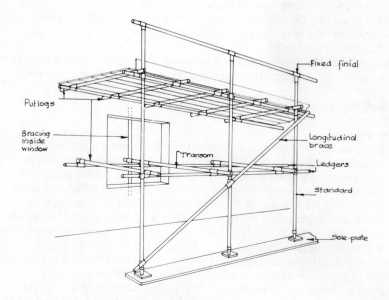

Fig. 8.2 Putlog scaffolding

72

iii) *Mobile*   Generally used in maintenance work, this scaffold is in the form of a tower mounted on wheels. It may be erected using either metal tubes and fittings or prefabricated 'H' frames having integral couplings (fig. 8.3).

iv) *System*   Many manufacturers of scaffolding produce their own systems. The object of the system is to eliminate as many loose fittings as possible and also to use standard lengths for standards, ledgers, and transoms (fig. 8.4).

v) *Trestle* (fig. 8.5)   Used for quick access to those levels just out of reach of a person standing on the floor where a ladder would be unsuitable. The support is provided by a ladder trestle, an 'H' frame, a puncheon frame, or adjustable split (fork) heads with a timber bearer.

vi) *Ladders* (fig. 8.6), generally of timber to BS 1129 or aluminium to BS 2037, are the usual means of gaining access to high-level platforms, but on large contracts the building itself or a passenger hoist may also be used.

b) Comparison
i) *Independent*   Suitable for the majority of working situations. It involves a lot of work in both erection and dismantling, together with the use of easily lost expensive fittings.

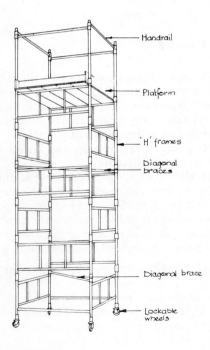

Fig. 8.3   Mobile scaffolding

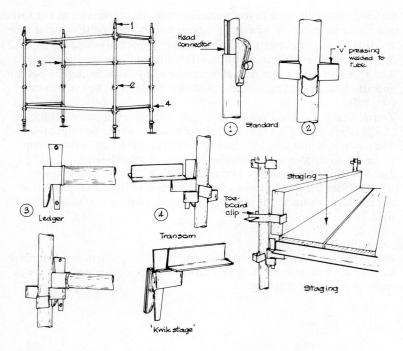

Fig. 8.4 System scaffolding

ii) *Putlog* Suitable for maintenance work where the existing wall into
which it is built is suitably strong. This scaffold uses less tube and
fittings than the independent variety but is slower to erect by virtue of
the building-in process. The working face is not obstructed by standards
as it is by the inner row in the independent scaffold.

iii) *Mobile* Suitable where there is an even level surface to move upon and
the work is not accessible by ladder.

iv) *System* Similar advantages to the independent scaffold, but is much
easier and quicker to erect and dismantle, and the number of fittings
lost is reduced to a minimum. Standard bay sizes improve safety by use
of a standardised scaffold board but prove difficult when the building's
length is not a straightforward number of bay multiples. Adjustable
baseplates are required to give level transoms and ledgers.

The materials used in the above types are 48 mm outside-diameter tube
and timber boards.

There are two types of tube — steel and aluminium-alloy. The steel tube
to BS 1139 is some three times stronger than the alloy tube, but also three
times heavier. It may be galvanised for protection but is still susceptible to
corrosion. The alloy tube, also to BS 1139, does not require protection unless
it comes into contact with materials such as wet lime, cement, and sea water.

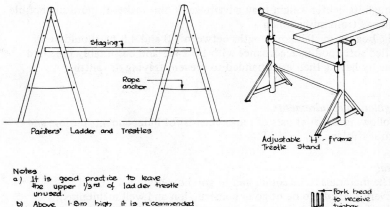

Staging

Rope anchor

Painters' Ladder and Trestles

Adjustable 'H' - Frame
Trestle Stand

Notes
a) It is good practice to leave the upper 1/3rd of ladder trestle unused.

b) Above 1·8m high it is recommended that the platform or staging should be high enough for work to be carried out in a sitting position.

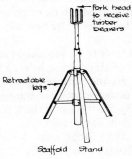

Fork head to receive timber bearers

Retractable legs

Scaffold Stand

Fig. 8.5 Trestles

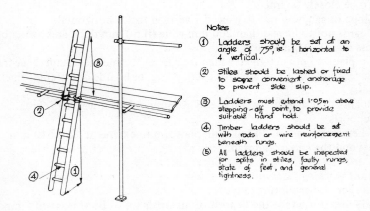

Notes

① Ladders should be set at an angle of 75°, ie. 1 horizontal to 4 vertical.

② Stiles should be lashed or fixed to some convenient anchorage to prevent side slip.

③ Ladders must extend 1·05m above stepping-off point, to provide suitable hand hold.

④ Timber ladders should be set with rods or wire reinforcement beneath rungs.

⑤ All ladders should be inspected for splits in stiles, faulty rungs, state of feet, and general tightness.

Fig. 8.6 Ladders

Although its lighter weight is an advantage, it also makes it more susceptible to damage from mishandling.

The boards, in standard lengths between 2.0 and 4.8 m, should be of specified softwood in accordance with BS 2482 and be suitably prepared for use by having their ends banded to prevent fraying or splitting.

c) Regulation requirements
The following are brief lists of requirements for independent, putlog, and system scaffolds.

General
1. The materials to be sound and of good quality.
2. Every scaffold to be of good construction and well maintained.
3. Scaffolds not to be partially dismantled (unless this complies with regulations).
4. Standards to be vertical or leaning towards the building.
5. Foot of standard to be on a firm base.
6. Ledgers and putlogs to be horizontal and securely fastened.
7. The distance between transoms or putlogs not to exceed
    1.0 m for 31 mm thick planking,
    1.5 m for 38 mm,
    2.59 m for 50 mm.
8. Scaffolds to be properly supported, strutted, and braced, or connected to the building to ensure stability.
9. No part of the building to be used to support the scaffold unless structurally sound.
10. Loads on the scaffold should be evenly distributed.

Working platforms and gangways
1. To be closely boarded.
2. Slope of gangway not to exceed 1 vertical to 1.5 horizontal.
3. Boards not to be less than 200 mm wide (if 50 mm thick and over, not less than 150 mm wide).
4. No plank to project greater than four times its thickness (unless secured).
5. Bevelled pieces to be used for overlapping, or boards of different thickness.
6. Boards to rest securely and evenly on supports (not less than three supports).
7. When work done at end of wall, platform to extend at least 610 mm beyond the end of the wall.

Widths of working platforms
1. 635 mm if for footing only.
2. 863 mm if used for the deposit of materials (must be at least 430 mm between material and edge).
3. Gangways at least 430 mm wide (635 mm if for passage of materials).

4. If platform becomes slippery, remedy by sanding or cleaning. Platform to be kept free from rubbish, unnecessary obstruction, and projecting nails.

Guard rails and toe boards
These apply if a person is liable to fall more than 2 m.
1. Guard-rail required between 900 mm and 1.165 mm above platform.
2. Toe board to be not less than 150 mm in height.
3. Toe board to be fixed inside uprights.
4. Distance between toe boards and guard-rail should not exceed 762 mm.

Trestle scaffolds
1. Trestles to be set on firm level base.
2. Not to be used if person liable to fall more than 4.57 m.
3. No trestle scaffold to be erected on top of scaffold unless space allowed for transport of materials.
4. Trestle to be firmly attached to platform.
5. Trestles not more than 1.37 m apart when using 38 mm thick boards or 2.4 m apart for 50 mm boards.

Ladders
1. All ladders to be of good construction.
2. Not to be used if rung is missing.
3. Rungs to be properly fixed to stiles.
4. To have firm and level footing.
5. To be secured to prevent undue swaying.
6. To be fixed at upper resting place and to extend at least 1 m above platform.
7. If above 9.14 m high, provide intermediate landing space.

Inspection of scaffolds
1. Must be inspected by competent person, within seven days.
2. Inspect if subjected to adverse weather conditions.
3. Reports to be made on prescribed form detailing
   location and description,
   date of inspection,
   result of such inspection, and
   signed by person making inspection.
4. Reports to be kept on site.

8.3 Fittings (fig. 8.7)
Apart from the specialist items used in the erection of system scaffolding — e.g. standards, transoms, ledgers, and braces — there is a wide variety of steel or aluminium fittings used in conjunction with both system and tube scaffolding.

Adjustable baseplate   Baseplate incorporating screw-jack for adjusting levels.

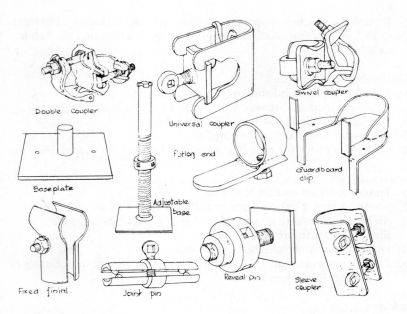

Fig. 8.7 Fittings

Baseplate	Square plate with locating spigot fitting into foot of standard, to spread load.
Coupler:	
double	Joins ledgers to standards.
purlin	Used to fix timber members to tube framework.
putlog	Joins putlog or transom to ledger.
sleeve	Joins two tubes end to end externally.
swivel	Joins two tubes at any angle.
Finial clip	Secures handrail to top of standard.
Fork head	U-shaped housing to carry bearers.
Joint pin	Joins two tubes end to end internally.
Putlog head or end	Fixed to end of tube to convert it into a putlog.
Reveal pin	Tightens a tube between two opposing surfaces.
Toe-board clip	Fixes toe board to standard.

9   Framed structures

Understands the construction of steel and in-situ r.c. framed structures.

  9.1   Identifies universal columns, universal beams, and standard angles and channels.
  9.2   Describes and sketches methods of connecting steel members together using bolts and welding methods.
**9.3   *Prepares details of column-to-base, beam-to-column, beam-to-beam and column splice.*
  9.4   Describes the erection procedure for a simple steel frame not exceeding four storeys high.
  9.5   Sketches methods of providing up to two hours' fire resistance to steel structural members.
  9.6   Sketches and describes typical arrangements of mild-steel reinforcement to column and beams.
  9.7   Sketches and describes further examples of formwork construction.
  9.8   Describes the erection procedure for an r.c. frame up to four storeys high.

Acknowledgement is due to the Technician Education Council for permission to use the content of the TEC units in this chapter. The council reserves the right to amend the content of its units at any time.

9.1 Steel sections

Structural steelwork from which the framework or components of a building are fabricated is manufactured in a number of quality grades and rolled in accordance with BS 4, 'Structural steel sections'. Part 1 of the standard deals with 'hot-rolled sections' and part 2 with 'hot-rolled hollow sections' (fig. 9.1).

The hot-rolled sections include
a)   universal beam with tapered flanges (UB),
b)   universal beam with parallel flanges (UB),
c)   universal column (UC),
d)   joist (still referred to by many as RSJ),
e)   channel,
f)   unequal angle,
g)   equal angle,
h)   T-bar — various types available,
j)   universal bearing pile — similar to the column, but flange and web thicknesses are equal.

The rolled hollow sections include
k)   circular,
l)   square,
m)   rectangular.

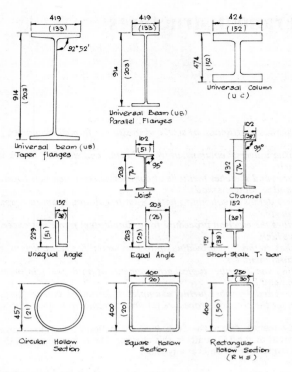

Fig. 9.1 Typical structural steel sections

9.2 Bolted and welded joints

The methods of jointing structural steel sections are bolting, welding, and riveting; however, riveting is now seldom used, on the grounds of cost and reliability, particularly for site work.

a) *Bolts*   There are several types of bolt.
   i)   Black bolts, BS 4190, are cheap because of their low strength and fairly wide dimensional tolerance — from which their name derives. These bolts should be used only in low-stress situations.
   ii) Bright bolts are machined to much closer tolerances than the black but have similar strength characteristics.
   iii) Friction-grip bolts, BS 4395, manufactured from high-tensile steel, are designed to transfer the load from one structural member to another by friction between the faces of the members rather than by the dowel effect of (i) and (ii). In order to achieve the required friction, the bolt must be tightened to a predetermined torque or compressive stress using a torque wrench or load-indicator washers.

The members to be joined are usually predrilled before arrival on site, which allows greater dimensional control. The number and location of the holes depend on the amount of load to be transferred and the effect

80

of that load on the section, particularly having regard to the amount of material removed in drilling. The holes for black bolts should be 1.5 mm larger in diameter than the nominal bolt diameter, while 0.5 mm would be adequate tolerance for the other bolts, and because of localised stress there should be minimum distances between the holes — see fig. 9.2.

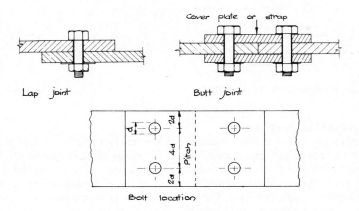

Fig. 9.2 Bolt details

b) *Welding* Welding eliminates much of the packing, drilling, and machining required for bolted connections but is difficult to supervise on site. It gives greater rigidity to the joint and in many instances removes the need for cover plates, thereby reducing material content in the structure. The length of weld is determined by the size of the weld and the amount of load to be transferred.

There are two main methods of welding: oxy–acetylene and electric-arc.

i) In oxy–acetylene welding, a mixture of oxygen and acetylene (a compound of carbon and hydrogen) is ignited to give a flame at a temperature of between 2000 and 3000 °C. This temperature is sufficient to melt steel and is one way in which steel may be cut. In the case of welding, the faces of the two members to be joined become molten and the metal in the welding rod fuses with them to 'reinforce' the joint.

ii) In electric-arc welding, the heat required to melt the faces is provided by an electric arc struck between the parent metal and a flux-coated welding-rod electrode. The current (approx. 100 V) is provided from a transformer, with the arc of short length also melting the electrode. This method is much faster than gas welding and gives a deeper metal penetration.

The various types of weld and associated terminology are shown in fig. 9.3.

81

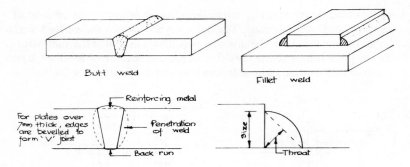

Fig. 9.3 Welded-joint terminology

9.3 Steelwork connections

a) *Column-to-base*   A steel column is able to carry a relatively large vertical
load in a relatively small cross-sectional area. In order to spread this load
into the foundation, a steel baseplate is attached to the end of the column
to act as the initial load-spreader and resist the punching action of the
column through the plate. The load-transference from column to base is
achieved by either a gusset base or a slab or bloom base.

   i) Gusset base (fig. 9.4(a))   The load is gradually transferred from the
    column to the base by the use of gusset plates and angles. This
    reduces the punching shear and enables a thin baseplate to be used.

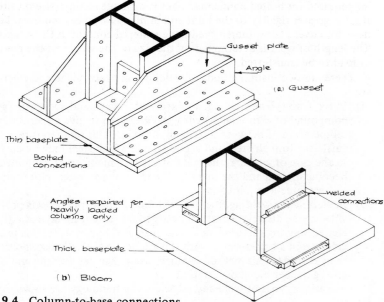

Fig. 9.4   Column-to-base connections

82

ii) Slabs or bloom base (fig. 9.4(b))   The column bears directly on the baseplate and is held in position only by the bolted or welded connection. Since there is direct load-transference from column to base, the face of the baseplate and the end of the column should be machined to permit even load-spread. The plate, being directly loaded and having to resist all the punching shear stresses, will be much thicker than that used for the gusset base.

b) *Beam-to-column*   The load from the main beams is transferred to the column by means of cleats bolted or welded to the web and the top and bottom flanges of the beam — see fig. 9.5. The beams at the top of the

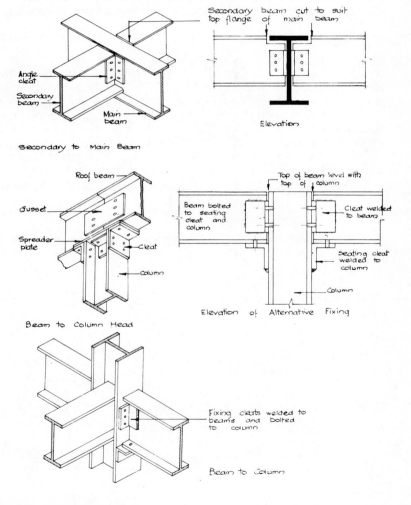

Fig. 9.5   Beam connections

83

structure may be connected similarly or, alternatively, by means of a bearing connection in which the beams rest on a bearing cap or plate fixed to the top of the column. In order to reduce the amount of work on site, the cleats are fixed to one or other of the members before leaving the prefabrication shop. This shop fitting also improves the accuracy of the work.

c) *Beam-to-beam*   The method of connection will depend upon the nature of construction, but in the majority of cases the top flanges are level. This means that the top flange of the secondary beam together with a section of the web must be cut away in order to accommodate the top flange of the main beam. The connection is generally by web cleats, although a seating cleat may be used for main beams having deep webs.

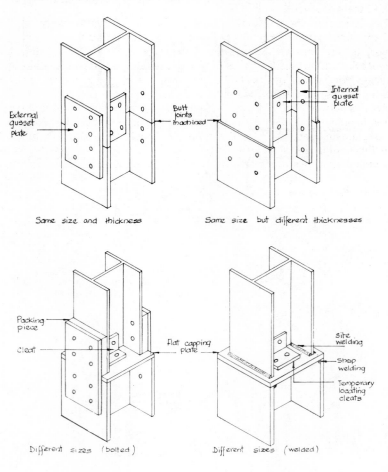

Fig. 9.6   Column-splice details

d) *Column splice*   The joining together of two column sections may be required because the column is too long to be delivered to site in one length or it is more economical to reduce the column section at a higher level because of reduced loading conditions. These connections are generally made near floor level, just above a column-to-beam connection. The major consideration in jointing is the preservation of axial (centre-line) loading. In the case of different-size sections, a capping plate is attached to the head of the lower column by shop welding and the upper column is located centrally on the plate by bolting or welding on site; for similar sized sections, machined ends and cover plates are all that are required (fig. 9.6).

9.4 Steelwork erection

This consists of the erection, on prepared bases, of prefabricated units. Since the prefabrication is accurate and erection tolerances are small, the setting-out work on site must also be accurate. Tolerances may be built into the column-base location by casting the holding-down bolts into the pad foundation in such a way as to afford small lateral movement (fig. 9.7), the top of the base being kept some 10 mm below the required height to allow for level deficiencies between the various column bases. The columns are located on the holding-down bolts and packed up to level using steel shims between the baseplate and pad (fig. 9.8). The columns are held approximately plumb by inclined adjustable steel props and vertical wind braces incorporated in the overall design. Beams are attached to the columns for at least the first two

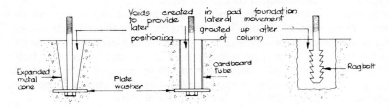

Fig. 9.7   Holding-down bolts

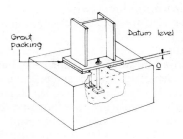

Fig. 9.8   Column anchorage

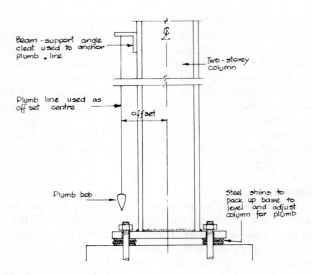

Beam - support angle
cleat used to anchor
plumb . line

Two - storey
column

Plumb line used as
off set centre

offset

Plumb bob

Steel shims to
pack up base to
level and adjust
column for plumb

Fig. 9.9 Column positioning

storeys prior to the final locating, and plumbing and anchoring down of the columns are achieved by a theodolite and offset centre line (fig. 9.9). Any gap between column base and pad is grouted solid using neat cement (< 25 mm) or 1:2 sand:cement mix (> 25 mm).

The erection of steelwork involves the use of heavy lifting equipment such as a crane. The provision of shop-fixed seating cleats on the columns allows the beams to bear on these cleats during accurate location, with only the sway associated with support by crane hook. The accurate lining up of bolt holes is by hand leverage on a podger. Where site in-situ welding is carried out, it is usual for the members being joined to be rigidly clamped together or temporarily bolted together by cleats or fish-tail plates.

Once the lower storeys of the frame have been accurately fixed, the structural floors (p.c. units) may be incorporated prior to completion of the steel frame. This may
a)   allow a shortening of the programme;
b)   allow other inside works to proceed;
c)   provide a working platform for structural erection, particularly for column splicing;
d)   stiffen the structure.

Most steelwork arrives on site ready primed and, because of this, care should be taken in the handling, storage, and erection operations. Timber packings should be used between members when stored and between member and sling when lifting and placing, to ensure that the priming coat is not damaged. Further corrosion protection should be applied as soon as practicable after completion of the framework, to minimise the risk of damage from this source.

9.5 Fire protection

Steel, being formed by heat, is also affected by it. At a temperature of 400 to 500 °C, structural steel begins to loose its strength; by 800 °C it will have lost up to two thirds of its strength; and by 1200 °C it will be semi-liquid. Most fires in buildings reach temperatures of 700 °C, and it is therefore essential that the steelwork be protected if the building frame is to be preserved in the event of fire, not only for future rebuilding but also for the safe exit of the occupants during the fire as well as safe entry and exit of fire-fighting teams.

The Building Regulations 1976, section E1(5), schedule 8, part V, give details of the various materials and thicknesses which are acceptable for providing various periods of fire resistance. Typical requirements are shown in figs 9.10 and 9.11.

9.6 Reinforcement of concrete

The student should by now be well aware that concrete is weak in tension and reasonably strong in compression; hence the need, in structural design, to reinforce the concrete with steel bars designed to carry those forces that the concrete is unable to carry.

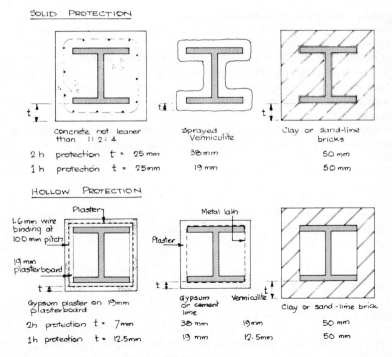

Fig. 9.10 Fire protection to steel columns

87

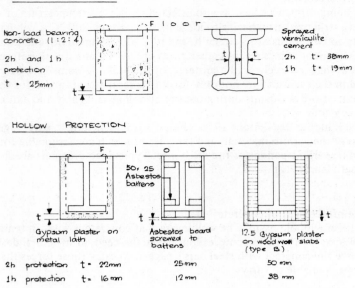

Fig. 9.11　Fire protection to steel beams

The main forces (fig. 9.12) which must be considered are
tension resulting from bending of member,
compression from bending,
compression from direct loading,
shear.
The maximum values of these forces and their location are determined by
calculation and the use of bending-moment and shear-force diagrams.

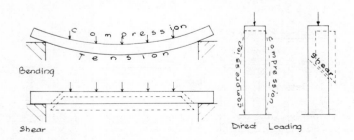

Fig. 9.12　Forces in members

The amount of reinforcement required in a structural member is determined by the designer in accordance with the recommendations of British

Standard Code of Practice CP 110, 'The structural use of concrete'. In designing the reinforcement, he must consider the following aspects:
ease of bending to required shape;
ability of concrete to transfer forces into the reinforcement, i.e. bond;
the amount of strain the reinforcement is capable of carrying without weakening;
the tensile and compressive strength of the reinforcing bars;
location within the structural member for optimum effect;
ready and economic availability.

Steel bars generally fulfil all the above requirements, or can be modified to do so. Such modifications include deformed or bent bars for improved bond (fig. 9.13) and various qualities of steel — mild steel and high-yield-strength-steel being most common. The location within a member must be a compromise: the optimum would be at the face of the member, but in such a situation the bars would be exposed to fire and corrosion and, since the concrete would not surround them, their bond would be weak. The minimum amounts of cover to the reinforcement recommended in CP 110, i.e. the distance between the concrete face and the bar closest to the face, are shown in extract in fig. 9.14.

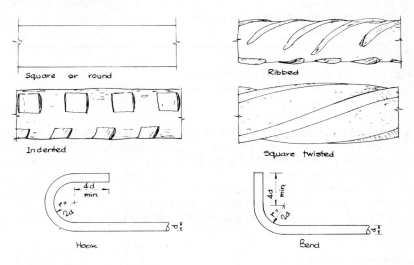

Fig. 9.13 Deformed and bent bars

In communicating his wishes to the erection team, the designer uses detail drawings and reinforcement schedules. The schedules itemise the various bar types shown on the drawing, while the drawing indicates the location of a component within the overall framework, the size of component, the location of the reinforcement together with specific details which complement information on the schedule, cover, and concrete quality. To abbreviate the information on drawings relating to reinforcement, a coding system is employed.

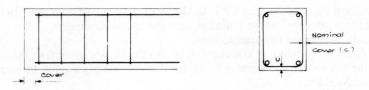

| | Concrete grade | | | | |
| Condition of exposure | 20 | 25 | 30 | 40 | 50 |
	Nominal cover (mm)				
Mild — completely protected against weather.	25	20	15	15	15
Moderate—sheltered from severe rain and freezing; buried concrete; concrete continuously under water.	—	40	30	25	20
Severe — exposed to driving rain and freezing; subject to heavy condensation or corrosive fumes.	—	50	40	30	25
Very severe — exposed to sea water or moorland water.	—	—	—	60	50

Fig. 9.14 Nominal cover to reinforcement

A typical example would be 20 R 1604—250, which is interpreted as follows:
    20 = number of bars in the group or similar location
     R = bar type — mild-steel round bar
    16 = bar diameter (mm)
    04 = bar reference or mark number
    250 = spacing or distance between centres of bars
    A typical detail drawing and schedule for a simple beam is shown in fig.
9.15.

a) Column reinforcement

The column is generally a vertical member transmitting loads from one level to another. These loads, created by walls, floors, and beams, are seldom wholly compressive in nature, and while concrete is strong in compression it must generally be reinforced to take account of the various loading conditions. A column will bend either as a result of buckling from a combination of load and slenderness (large height-to-width ratio) or as a result of the beam connections (fig. 9.16). This bending will create additional compression as well as inducing tension in the members. Where there is compressive loading, a shearing or bursting effect (fig. 9.16) can also occur.

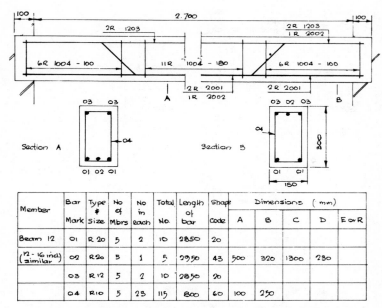

Member	Bar Mark	Type # Size	No of Mbrs	No in each	Total No.	Length of bar	Shape Code	Dimensions (mm)				
								A	B	C	D	E or R
Beam 12	01	R 20	5	2	10	2850	20					
(12 - 16 incl.) similar	02	R 20	5	1	5	2950	43	500	320	1300	230	
	03	R 12	5	2	10	2850	20					
	04	R 10	5	23	115	800	60	100	250			

NB. Shape, code, and dimensions in accordance with BS 4466

Fig. 9.15 Typical beam reinforcement

The longitudinal reinforcement in a column is designed to accommodate direct compression and bending effects, while the lateral reinforcement provides for the shear stresses.

Columns are generally symmetrical in shape and should have a minimum of four main reinforcing bars in the cross-section (six for a circular column) each with a diameter of at least 12 mm and having a total cross-sectional area equal to at least 1% of the gross column section — see fig. 9.17. The lateral reinforcement, termed links or binders, should have a diameter at least a quarter of that of the main bars (min. 5 mm) and be set at intervals or at a pitch of the smallest of
 i)   300 mm,
 ii) least lateral column dimension,
 iii) twelve times the diameter of smallest main bars.
Circular columns may have helical reinforcement set at a similar pitch. All binders are set around the main steel and fixed in place with 16 s.w.g. (1.6 mm) soft-iron tie wire.

For ease of construction the width of a column and the width of an intersecting beam are the same, and, since there will be a similar cover to the reinforcement in both cases, a clash of bars is likely to occur. In such instances one set of bars must be cranked to avoid the clash, and it is general practice to move the column bars (fig. 9.17).

91

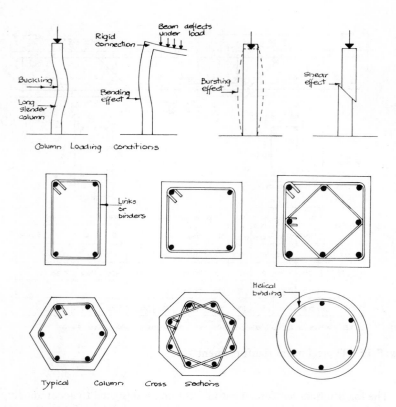

Fig. 9.16 Concrete columns

b) Beam reinforcement

Beams which support walls and floors may be designed in a similar manner to floor slabs, i.e. simple, restrained, continuous, and cantilever. Each method of design imposes a variety of loading and bending conditions upon the beam, but in essence the forces are compression, tension, and shear.

The main reinforcement is designed to carry the maximum bending moment but, as that moment changes for different positions on the beam, the requirement for reinforcement is also changed. This may allow the designer to curtail bars or alternatively make use of them for other purposes where the moment is reduced. For example, in the case of continuous or restrained beams, the tension zone changes from the bottom to the top of a beam in the region of the support; hence reinforcement can be seen changing from one face to the other and at the same time, during that transition, being used to provide additional shear resistance, see fig. 9.18. Further shear resistance is provided by vertical links or stirrups (similar to the binders in a column), which also provide against shrinkage cracking. The spacing of these links must be designed, because the shear force on a beam is changing from a minimum

92

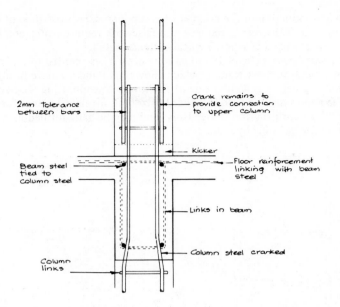

Fig. 9.17 Column-and-beam junction

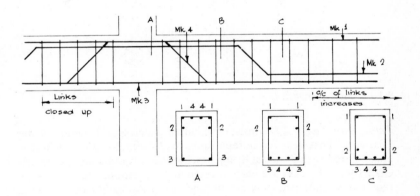

Fig. 9.18 Shear reinforcement in beams

value around the mid-span region to a maximum at the supports; hence the links are generally closer together near the support than they are at mid-span.

9.7 Formwork
Since formwork forms such a large part of the cost of an in-situ concreting operation, many formwork systems have been devised in an attempt to reduce those costs. The main considerations in designing such systems are standard-

93

isation and reduction in the number of components, reduced time of erection and stripping of the forms, reduction in falsework requirements, and improvement in reuse characteristics. Typical systems include

a) *Standard panels* (fig. 9.19) of various sizes. These consist of a ply facing on a metal support framing which allows tight and accurate location of abutting panels as well as ease of anchorage to supporting falsework. The panels may be used in either horizontal or vertical planes for slab and wall construction respectively, and may be gang-formed into larger units for handling by crane.

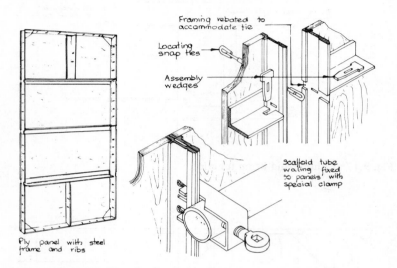

Framing rebated to accommodate tie

Locating snap ties

Assembly wedges

Scaffold tube waling fixed to panels with special clamp

Ply panel with steel frame and ribs

Fig. 9.19   Panel formwork

b) *Table forms* (fig. 9.20) consist of standard panels and their supporting falsework. They are used in repetitious in-situ concrete floors where a crane, fitted with a special lifting bracket, can lift out a complete section. Once the foot jacks have been lowered and repositioned at the next required position, the only erection necessary is an adjustment of the foot jacks to bring the soffit to the required level.

Other formwork operations include

c) The *surrounding of steel beams* in concrete for structural and fire-protection purposes. This may be carried out in a similar manner to an in-situ beam or by using the structural steelwork for support (fig. 9.21).

d) *Vertical walls*   As with columns, the pressure increases with the depth of concrete poured, and, in order to maintain a standard wall width without excessive external falsework, consumable steel ties are used to pro-

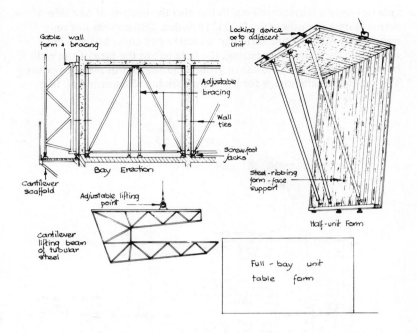

Fig. 9.20 Table formwork

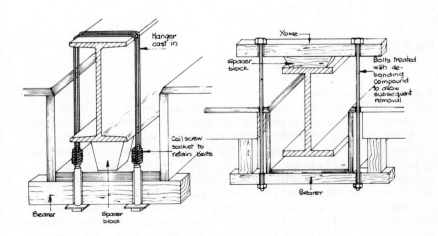

Fig. 9.21 Formwork to steel beams

95

vide not only a correct wall width but also the bracing of one side of forms against the other (fig. 9.22). Threaded plastic cores not only ensure that the ties have sufficient concrete end cover but also are removable for reuse after casting, the hole left in the face of the wall being made good with mortar or grout. The ties cast in previous pours also provide an anchorage for the formwork in subsequent wall lifts.

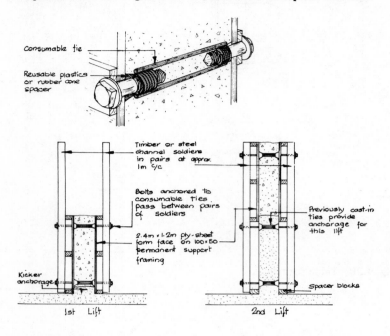

Fig. 9.22 Wall ties

9.8 R.C. frame erection

The erection of an in-situ reinforced-concrete beam-and-column building frame begins at foundation level with the pad, the reinforcement to the pad being linked to the column by column starter bars (fig. 9.23). A kicker (see volume 2, fig. 7.3) is cast integral with the pad or while the pad concrete is 'green'. If ground beams are being incorporated into the design, a stub column is cast up to the soffit of the ground beams, whose reinforcement is linked to that in the column prior to the casting of the beams.

Once the beams are cast or, alternatively if no ground beams are included, after the casting of column kickers on the pad, a prefabricated cage of column reinforcement, whose height extends some 750 mm above the first-floor level, is fixed to the column starter bars. The height of the column starter bars and the height of the cage should allow sufficient splice length for the loads in the reinforcement to be transferred from one set of bars to the lower

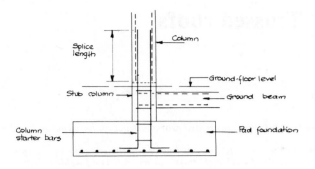

Fig. 9.23 Column starter bars

set without encroaching on concrete already cast. Spacer blocks are attached to the reinforcement prior to the fixing and plumbing and bracing of the column forms. Beam starter bars may be incorporated by tying them to the existing column reinforcement and leaving them either projecting through or over the formwork in the shape of inverted 'L' or by bending them down and anchoring them to the face of the formwork for subsequent bending back into position after casting. For continuous beams, the reinforcement will also be continuous over the support and may not require column starters. Where panel walls are to be constructed abutting the column, suitable fixings may be incorporated attached to the face of the shutters (see chapter 11).

The concrete in the column is poured to a height some 25 mm above the soffit of the lowest connecting beam by means of a tremie tube, inserted from above through the centre of the reinforcing cage. The tremie is slowly withdrawn as the level of the concrete rises, care being taken to ensure that the lower end of the tube is always covered by concrete. This method of pouring ensures a minimum segregation of the aggregates during pouring. The concrete is consolidated by means of a slim poker vibrator or an external vibrator, and care should be taken in vibration to ensure that the various layers during the pour are effectively joined together and all air is removed.

After stripping, the beam forms are erected and, if an integral floor slab is to be cast, the formwork to the slab soffit will also be erected and levelled prior to the insertion of the beam reinforcing cages and slab reinforcement where applicable, the beam starter bars being spliced to the main bars of the beam cages. In large operations, concrete may be poured into the beams up to 25 mm above slab soffit level, either before the casting of the slab or even in some cases before the slab forms are erected. Once the concrete has cured, column kickers are cast on the slab and the sequence is repeated or, in the case of a 'pure' framework, specially made column forms are anchored or clipped over the existing work from which the subsequent column shuttering is erected, after the next section of cage reinforcement has been spliced on.

97

10   Trussed roofs

Understands the principles of trussed roof construction for spans up to 12 m.

**10.1 *Explains the necessity for roof trusses and the principle of triangulation.*
  10.2 *Draws details of steel angle trusses using bolted and welded connections.*
  10.3 *Draws details of sheet coverings and insulation, including details at eaves, ridge, and verge.*
**10.4 *Draws details of the TRADA standard roof truss.*
  10.5 *Describes the principles of timber connection using toothed-plate and split-ring connectors.*

Acknowledgement is due to the Technician Education Council for permission to use the content of the TEC units in this chapter. The council reserves the right to amend the content of its units at any time.

10.1 Roof trusses

A roof truss is a structural member which supports the purlins in roof construction. Depending upon the materials used in their construction and the design shape, trusses may span up to 30 m. The truss is therefore an important item in design consideration, particularly in situations where there is a requirement for large clear unobstructed floor areas for office, factory, or warehouse accommodation.

The ability to span large distances arises from two factors:
a)   the high strength-to-weight ratio of the materials used (i.e. steel, alloys, and timber) which permits an increase in loading or an increase in span because of the small value of self-weight of the member itself;
b)   the design of the truss in the form of a series of triangles.

The principle of triangulation in structural members was appreciated as early as the fifteenth century, but it was not until the latter half of the nineteenth century that the structural mechanics and interaction of the various members were appreciated and subsequently investigated in detail. The basis of triangulation is the fact that if three members are joined together, no matter how loosely, at their ends to form a triangle, that shape will remain unaltered unless one or more of the members is stretched or buckled. In theory, provided that the joints are considered to be 'hinged', all the members will be subjected to only tension or compression; however, in practice there is a certain amount of rigidity at the joint, inducing bending in the framework members which in turn can provide the designer with additional strength in the framework over and above the values indicated by simple design procedures.

There are a variety of roof-truss configurations (see fig. 10.1), all of which incorporate the triangulation principle.

98

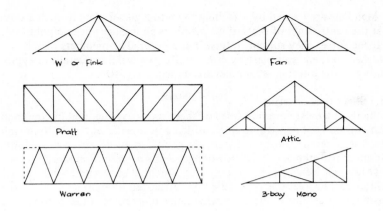

Fig. 10.1 Types of roof truss

10.2 Steel trusses

In order to construct trusses in steel, angle and 'T' sections are used. These sections provide the strength and rigidity required of members in such a frame, while at the same time having a good strength-to-weight ratio and easy handling and fixing characteristics.

Increased strength and rigidity for members in compression within a truss is achieved by joining two angles 'back-to-back' to form a 'T' section.

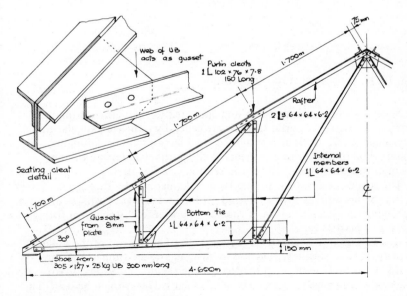

Fig. 10.2 Steel-roof-truss details

99

Members are jointed by attaching them to a gusset plate in such a way that the centre lines of the various members all intersect at one point, i.e. so that the forces they support intersect at a point. The members may be attached to the gusset plate by either bolting or welding. Details of typical joints and the jointing techniques are shown in fig. 10.2.

10.3 Sheet roof covering

Probably the most common form of sheet roof covering used in conjunction with trussed roof construction is profiled asbestos cement. It is non-combustible, not affected by rot or vermin, has good corrosion resistance, requires minimum maintenance, and provides good storm-water drainage.

Other lightweight sheet roof coverings include corrugated, galvanised, or plastics-coated steel sheets, profiled or corrugated aluminium, p.v.c., other plastics, or glass fibre. There is a wide range of profiles available in various standard sheet sizes for most of the materials mentioned – see fig. 10.3.

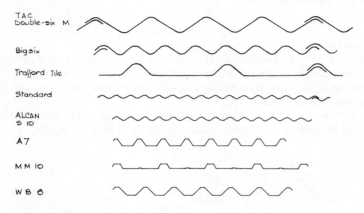

Fig. 10.3 Typical sheet-roofing profiles

Sheet roofing is supported on and anchored to the purlins spanning between trusses. The purlin sections are generally either rectangular timber, steel angle, or 'Z' section, but tubular steel sections are occasionally used. The method of anchoring the sheets to the purlin will depend on the material and the shape of the purlin section (see fig. 10.4).

The sheets are fixed by drilling 10 mm diameter holes through the crown of the corrugation, and the bolts and profiled washer are positioned before tightening the nut. Corrosion of the bolt is prevented by the final fitting of a protective plastics cap.

It is advisable to begin the laying of the roof at the end of the building away from the prevailing wind and to ensure correct fitting of the bargeboard. To comply with the provisions of the Health and Safety at Work Act and to avoid damage to the sheets, roof or cat ladders should be used. The amount of side and end laps between sheets will vary depending on the sheet

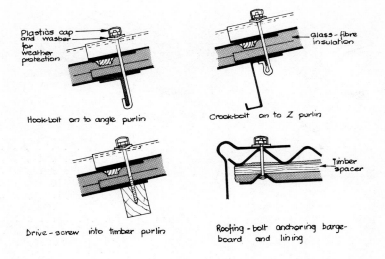

Plastics cap and washer for weather protection

Glass-fibre insulation

Hook-bolt on to angle purlin

Crook-bolt on to Z purlin

Timber spacer

Drive-screw into timber purlin

Roofing-bolt anchoring barge-board and lining

Fig. 10.4 Sheet-roofing anchorage

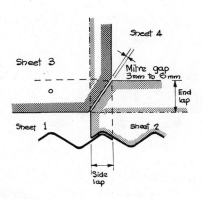

Sheet 4

Sheet 3

Mitre gap 3mm to 6mm

End lap

o

Sheet 1

Sheet 2

Side lap

Fig. 10.5 Mitred joint

profile and the pitch of the roof; however, where four sheets meet at a point, two of them should be mitred to overcome problems of a 'four-thickness' lap joint (see fig. 10.5). Specially shaped sections are produced by manufacturers to deal with situations such as at the ridge, eaves, and verge (figs 10.6 and 10.7).

The introduction of legislation (Building Regulations, section FF) relating to the standard of thermal insulation in the roofs of new properties other than domestic has meant that a sandwich construction of two layers of

101

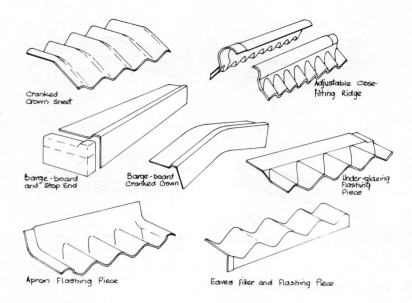

Fig. 10.6 Special profiles

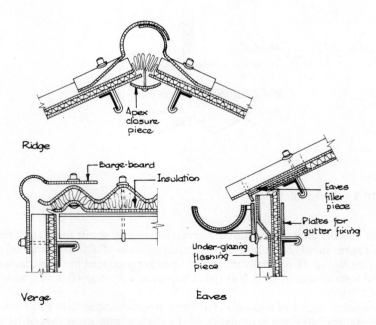

Fig. 10.7 Details at ridge, verge, and eaves

102

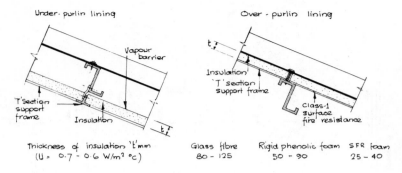

Fig. 10.8   Insulation standards

asbestos-cement sheeting with a glass-fibre-quilt core is probably one of the easier methods of construction which complies with the new regulations. Other forms of construction complying with the regulation are shown in fig. 10.8.

10.4 TRADA roof trusses
The Timber Research and Development Association (TRADA) publishes a wide range of standard roof-truss design sheets for both domestic and industrial purposes, with various truss types catering for different span, pitch, and loading requirements. A typical domestic truss is shown in fig. 10.9.

10.5 Timber connectors
Before the introduction of the timber connector, the jointing of timber structural framing members was by means of bolts or individually formed timber joints. In the case of the bolt, wider members were required because of its poor efficiency as a mechanical connector and stress problems where the timber was in contact with the bolt. The disadvantage of timber jointing is in the length of time taken to form such joints.

There are several forms of connector, each having advantages in a particular situation. The basic idea of a connector is a shallow dowel in contact with the faces of adjacent lap-jointed timber members. The connector, being of large diameter, is able to transmit the loading from one member to the other over a greater area of timber, thereby reducing the level of stress in the timber.

a)   *Toothed-plate connectors* (fig. 10.10)   These are round or square metal plates having projecting teeth around the edges. They are produced in single- or double-sided forms. The single-sided connector is used where prefabricated or easily demountable structures are required, each member being predrilled and a connector embedded, the connectors coming back to back with each other on assembly. The double-sided connector is cheaper than two single-sided connectors and is used where permanent joints are required. The bolt which completes the latter joint is mainly

103

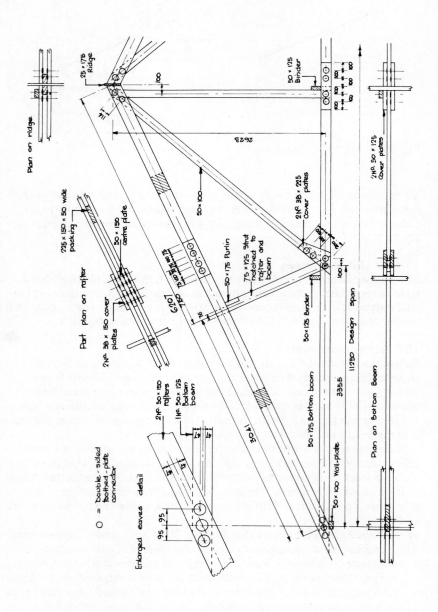

Fig. 10.9 TRADA roof truss

104

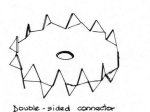
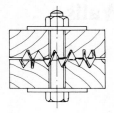

Double-sided connector

Fig. 10.10 Toothed-plate connector

to ensure that the members and connector(s) are held tightly in position; but, in the case of the single-sided connector, the load is passed directly to the bolt and the bolt should be capable of transmitting such loads. In both cases the teeth of the connector are embedded in the timber by pressure, no preformed groove being required.

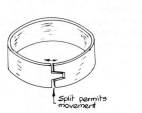
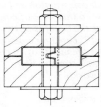

Split permits movement

Fig. 10.11 Split-ring connector

b) *Split-ring connectors* (fig. 10.11)   These consist of a simple circular band of metal with a split which permits differential movement between timber and metal without any appreciable stress increase. The band is embedded in a precut circular groove in the face of the members to be joined, each groove being half the depth of the ring. The bolt is again used to ensure that the timber members and connector are held tightly together. This joint has a higher load-carrying capacity than the toothed-plated connectors since there is a greater surface area of metal and timber in contact.

In order to prevent any long-term corrosive effects weakening the joint, all connectors should be galvanised.

105

11   Walls

Understands the construction of simple panel walls.

11.1   *Sketches and describes the construction of non-load-bearing brick panels, including methods of attachment to concrete.*

11.2   *Sketches and describes typical lightweight panel wall construction.*

Understands the principles of brick and concrete cross-wall construction.

*11.3   *Explains cross-wall construction in terms of structural and economic concepts of building and exemplifies the use of cross-walls together with their dependency on adjoining elements for stability.*

*11.4   *Describes the constraints imposed on the design team when employing cross-wall construction and identifies certain classes of building which are amenable to this form of construction.*

*11.5   *Evaluates the benefits of the erection and construction process itself when a building is based on cross-wall construction.*

*11.6   *Compares the merits of erection of types of structural material when used in cross-wall construction:*
    a)   brickwork,
    b)   blockwork,
    c)   no-fines concrete,
    d)   plain and reinforced concrete.

*11.7   *Describes those forms of concrete cross-wall construction which encourage the use of industrialised methods of construction.*

*11.8   *Details areas of cross-wall construction requiring special treatment and provision for structural and functional purposes.*

Acknowledgement is due to the Technician Education Council for permission to use the content of the TEC units in this chapter. The council reserves the right to amend the content of its units at any time.

Panel walls provide the envelope in skeleton-frame construction. They are designed to carry only their own weight together with wind loading on their face, and are supported at each floor — further restraint is provided by the columns and occasionally by the floor above (fig. 11.1).

11.1 Brick panel walls

The structural frame into which the panel is built may be hidden or featured, depending on the architectural style, and the panel itself may be formed in-situ or be precast.

Brick panel walls are generally constructed with cavities and an insulation-block inner leaf in order to comply with thermal-insulation regulations. As in traditional cavity walls, the external and internal leaves are linked together by ties.

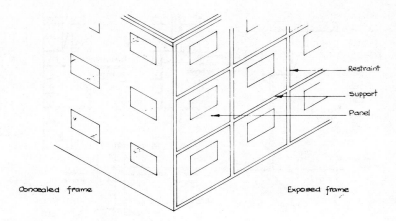

Fig. 11.1 Panel walls

The wall is supported on the lower floor with a damp-proof course incorporated in a similar manner to lintel construction, fig. 11.2, with the external face of the wall being set forward a small amount beyond the edge of the slab. This projection (fig. 11.3) provides a drip for the rain running down the wall face, or permits the introduction of narrow brick or tile slips which mask the concrete floor – thus giving the impression of a brick-built structure. The slips are held in position by steel plates, clips, anchors, epoxy- or polyester-resin mortars, or cement-based mortars with special bond-improving additives.

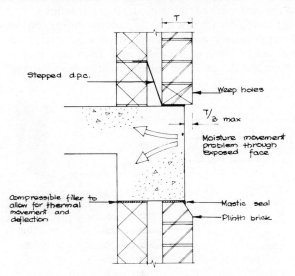

Fig. 11.2 Treatment at head and floor

107

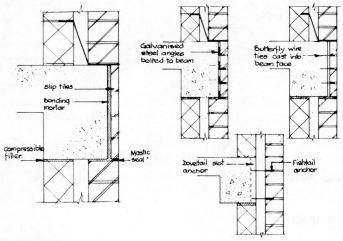

Fig. 11.3 Slip fixing

The head of the panel must also be provided with suitable damp-proofing treatment (fig. 11.2). Many maintenance problems arise in this area because of poor attention to damp-proofing at both design and construction stages. The problem is particularly evident where the floor edge is exposed as a result of moisture travelling through the concrete floor. In such instances it is advisable to provide the exposed concrete with a protective silicone treatment.

Lateral restraint of the panel is provided by anchorage at the columns, fig. 11.4, and the two most common methods are as follows.

a) Galvanised steel slots are cast into the column during construction, into which dovetail anchors are fitted and adjusted so as to be built into horizontal mortar joints of the panel wall. These slots may be incorporated on the external face of the column to provide anchorage to the facing

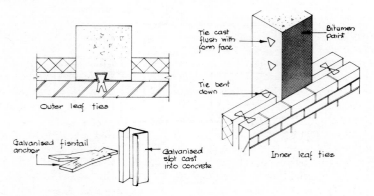

Fig. 11.4 Details of wall restraint

108

bricks, and in such cases it is usual for the bricks to abut the column and, in order to prevent moisture penetrating the column, the external face should be painted with bitumen.

b) Wire butterfly ties are cast into the column in such a way that one half of the tie may be pulled away from the face of the column to be embedded in the horizontal mortar joints while the other half remains firmly anchored in the column. This second method is much cheaper than the first but requires fairly accurate location of the ties prior to casting the columns, to ensure alignment with the brick joints.

11.2 Lightweight panel walls

Skeleton frames are designed to carry the whole of the structural loading of a building. This means that the infill panels have, with the exception of wind loading, no structural performance requirements. The panels, however, must still fulfil the other performance requirements of the external envelope. It is therefore possible to use a much lighter-weight construction than bricks, and this construction takes the form of two flat skins sandwiching suitable core materials and supported by a rigid frame. This can be expensive if the panels are purpose-made; therefore a manufacturer's system is chosen and the use of standard components is taken into account in the planning and design stages of the work.

The framing into which the panels are fitted is generally of timber or aluminium, thus permitting the easy incorporation of standard window frames of similar materials.

The external skin of the panel is either sheet steel with an enamelled facing, sheet aluminium, plastics sheet, or asbestos. Wide ranges of colour finishes and textures are also obtainable.

The thin sheet-metal external skins are supported on asbestos sheets which provide not only rigidity but also fire protection. Thermal and sound insulation is provided by the core in the form of either glass- or mineral-fibre boards or quilt, cork, fibreboard, polystyrene, or polyurethane. These materials also help to reduce the weight of the panel as compared to the more solid brick construction.

The internal skin must include some form of vapour barrier (usually aluminium foil) in order to prevent interstitial condensation occurring within the panel and at the same time provide a surface suitable for decoration. Suitable materials include plasterboard and asbestos board.

Where the core material lacks rigidity, the faces of the panel will be kept separated and parallel by means of a timber subframe, while in the case of a rigid core material the faces may be bonded directly to the core using suitable adhesives.

Details of the fixing of the panels into the frame and the frame into the structure are shown in figs 11.5 and 11.6. Special care must again be taken to ensure a weathertight joint between the panels and the framework, since there will be differential thermal and moisture movement between the two components. This is also true where two panels abut, although there the problem is not of the same magnitude.

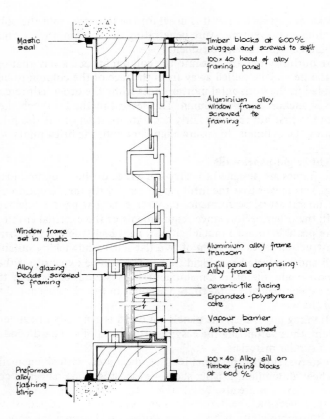

Mastic seal

Timber blocks at 600°/c plugged and screwed to soffit

100 × 40 head of alloy framing panel

Aluminium alloy window frame screwed to framing

Window frame set in mastic

Aluminium alloy frame transom

Infill panel comprising: Alloy frame

Alloy 'glazing' beads screwed to framing

Ceramic-tile facing

Expanded-polystyrene core

Vapour barrier

Asbestolux sheet

100 × 40 Alloy sill on timber fixing blocks at 600 °/c

Preformed alloy flashing strip

Fig. 11.5 Lightweight-metal panel walls

CROSS-WALL CONSTRUCTION

Cross-wall construction is the term applied to buildings in which the load-bearing walls are built at right angles to the length of the building (fig. 11.7).

11.3 Concepts of cross-wall construction
Structural Cross-walls support all floor and roof loads, thus setting up compressive stresses in the wall fabric. However, lateral restraint will be required to overcome problems of instability arising from
a) slenderness,
b) wind,
c) internal explosions.

These problems may be reduced by improving the rigidity of the structure using one or more of the following alternatives (fig. 11.8):
i) longitudinal structural internal walls in place of some lightweight partitions;

110

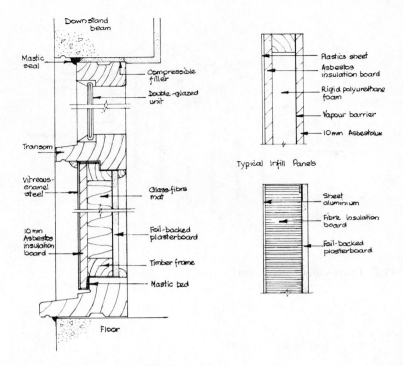

Fig. 11.6 Lightweight-timber panel walls

ii) rigid reinforced-concrete floors linked to the wall structure at suitable vertical intervals;

iii) the incorporation of piers (in the form of a 'T' or 'L' on plan) at the ends of the walls;

iv) the provision of stair or lift towers alongside the cross-walls, to act as buttresses.

Cross-wall construction over four or five storeys in height is generally termed a box frame, since the appearance is that of a series of open-ended boxes whose elevation is subsequently clad with panel walls, the structural frame being of reinforced concrete.

Economic This method of construction is economic because it is simple, repetitious, and lends itself to industrialised construction techniques. Cost savings are also effected because the walls, being internal, do not require damp or weather protection and generally run in straight lines.

11.4 Constaints of cross-wall construction
The cross-wall should be in the same vertical plane for the full height of the building and, while it provides excellent fire resistance and sound insulation,

111

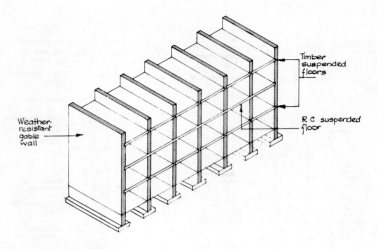

Fig. 11.7 Cross-wall construction

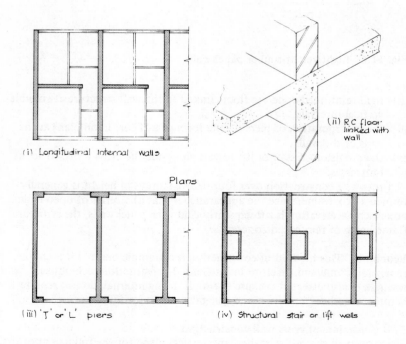

Fig. 11.8 Cross-wall rigidity

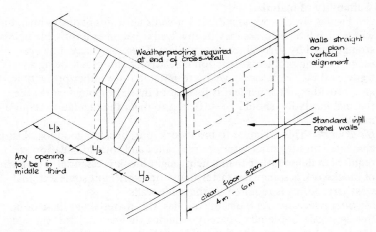

Walls straight on plan vertical alignment

Weatherproofing required at end of cross-wall

Standard infill panel walls

Any opening to be in middle third

clear floor span 4 m – 6 m

Fig. 11.9 Constraints

this limits the architect in respect of layout planning. Further restrictions on layout are imposed by structural-design and cost criteria. The former dictate that ideally there should be no openings through a cross-wall, but, where this is impractical, openings should be located within the middle third on plan (see fig. 11.9).

Cross-walls should be spaced at regular intervals along the length of the building, in order to standardise floor design and construction, the normal interval varying from 4 to 6 m. The optimum span is approximately 4.8 m, and such spans ensure economy of both flooring and cladding but severely restrict layout design.

Accommodation which is amenable to this form of repetitive small-scale layout tends to be domestic, e.g. terraced houses, flats, and maisonettes, as well as educational and hotel or hostel blocks.

11.5 Benefits of cross-wall construction

While the cross-wall spacing imposes constraints on the designer, it means that construction procedures are simplified. The walls and their foundations occur at standard intervals, thus making it easier to set out and check them with less chance of error. Being repetitious, they can be more easily and quickly constructed and so reduce costs. Both the structural and non-structural walls can be prefabricated or erected using industrialised processes, again reducing overall costs on large-scale projects.

Being internal and not requiring weather protection, the cross-walls can be designed as pure load-bearing units, which will result in optimum thickness and a reduction in both labour and material requirements when compared with external structural walls.

The external walls, being non-load-bearing, offer the designer a greater choice of materials and finishes, through which further cost savings may result.

113

11.6 Suitability of materials

a) *Brickwork*   Brickwork is suitable for walls up to four-storeys high, but where high lateral forces may be involved it becomes unsuitable unless strengthened by vertical reinforcing bars. These bars may, however, cause bonding problems. Erection is relatively cheap but, being a wet trade, is slow. Gable cavity walls are suitable for weather protection, and, providing the inner leaf is formed of insulation blockwork, the thermal insulation should be sufficient to meet the regulation requirements.

b) *Blockwork*   This is similar to brickwork, but, because good load-bearing characteristics together with fire resistance and sound insulation are required, a dense rather than a lightweight block is essential. The laying of blockwork is somewhat faster than brickwork, but some external weatherproofing is required on the gable walls.

c) *No-fines concrete*   As the name implies, this material has little or no fine aggregate in the mix, thereby reducing the material content and density but improving the thermal-insulation value to that of a plain concrete wall. Reinforcement in the form of steel mesh is required to improve the structural stability of this type of cross-wall. Provided that there are no openings or that any openings occur at the same point in every cross-wall, the walls may be cast in two-storey height increments to their full length in one pour. This reduces the erection period, and the standardisation ensures maximum reuse of formwork, particularly where a large number of walls are to be erected.

d) *Plain and reinforced concrete*   Structurally the most stable of cross-wall constructions, the same benefits apply as in (c) above in respect of formwork reuse. However, because of its greater density, the material will exert greater pressures on the formwork when poured, and it is therefore generally uneconomic to pour such walls in greater height increments than one storey.

11.7 Industrialised methods
Industrialised building is any method of building in which power, machinery, and mass-production methods are applied to the production process. It implies standardisation, continuity of production, integration of different stages, and mechanisation. The objectives of industrialisation are to increase productivity; to produce high environmental standards with reduced resources; and to move emphasis from site construction to site erection, using small teams of semi-skilled labour.

It will be appreciated that cross-wall construction immediately provides the standardisation which in turn leads to increased productivity by repetition.

a) *In-situ processes*   The process of constructing the box frame using large standard panel forms such as table forms (see fig. 9.20) with a no-fines or ordinary reinforced concrete provides an example of industrialisation on site.

b) *Prefabrication*   Cross-walls and other components such as floor units may be more economically produced in a factory, leaving only erection and finishing work to the personnel on site. Precast concrete is the common form of floor construction (see chapter 13), while precast concrete and brickwork are used for buildings exceeding two storeys. A prefabricated stressed skin of plywood on a timber frame is frequently used in conjunction with timber suspended-floor construction in two-storey domestic cross-wall construction.

11.8 Special requirements of cross-walls

Since the cross-wall is a relatively thin member, its slenderness can create structural instability unless provision for additional bracing or strengthening is made (see section 11.3).

The architect may wish to emphasise the vertical lines of the elevation by setting back both the floors and the infill panels from the building line of the cross-wall. In such cases, care must be taken to ensure that moisture penetration through the cross-wall into the accommodation unit does not occur. Typical methods of overcoming this problem are shown in fig. 11.10. Where the elevation of the building is flush, then a similar approach to that shown in figs 11.3 and 11.4 may be adopted.

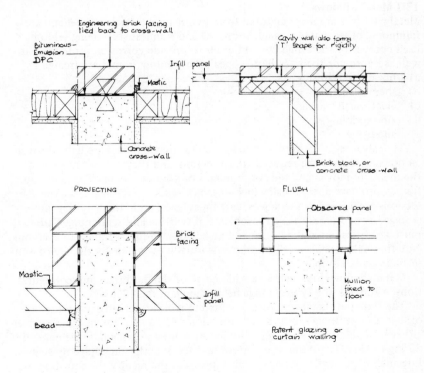

Fig. 11.10 Weatherproofing of cross-walls

115

12 Windows

Understands further examples of window construction.

   12.1 Identifies windows in coated steel and aluminium and describes methods of fixing to concrete.
**12.2 Explains the principle of patent glazing.*
**12.3 Sketches details of typical aluminium patent glazing.*

Acknowledgement is due to the Technician Education Council for permission to use the content of the TEC units in this chapter. The council reserves the right to amend the content of its units at any time.

12.1 Metal windows

Metal windows are manufactured from two main materials — steel and aluminium — other materials such as bronze and stainless steel being seldom used because of their high cost. In order to provide corrosion protection as well as improving their aesthetic appeal, the window frames are treated by

a)   hot-dip galvanising,
b)   sherardising,
c)   electro-galvanising,
d)   zinc spraying,
e)   anodising.

The advantages of metal windows are that they admit more light through an opening, due to the reduced frame section, and they are not subject to the moisture movement and rot problems of a timber frame. The aluminium frames also have a self-finish which does not require painting. Since the sections are welded at the angles, care must be taken in the handling and storage of the frames to avoid problems of twisting and scratching. Care must also be taken in the design and installation of metal frames to accommodate thermal movement; this problem is usually overcome by the use of non-setting mastic compounds.

Metal windows are made in a wide range of standard sizes and configurations, examples of a typical range being shown in fig. 12.1.

The fixing of metal windows to concrete is either directly or by the use of lugs. Direct fixing requires the formation of an anchorage in the concrete, either by drilling and plugging or by incorporating a fixing into the concrete during casting. The frame is predrilled and fixed to the anchorage by screws. Lug anchorage, while more expensive, provides the facility for adjusting the window position within certain limits by the use of slotted holes. The lug is fixed to the concrete by a drilled and plugged anchorage and screwed through

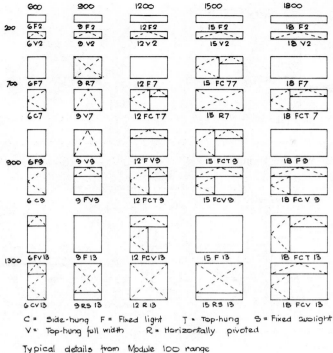

	600	900	1200	1500	1800
200	6 F2 / 6 V2	9 F2 / 9 V2	12 F2 / 12 V2	15 F2 / 15 V2	18 F2 / 18 V2
700	6F7 / 6 C7	9 R7 / 9 V7	12 F 7 / 12 FC T7	15 FC 77 / 15 R7	18 F7 / 18 FCT 7
900	6F9 / 6 C9	9 V9 / 9 FV9	12 F V9 / 12 FCT 9	15 FCT 9 / 15 FCV9	18 F9 / 18 Fc V 9
1300	6FV13 / 6 CV13	9 F 13 / 9 RS 13	12 FCV13 / 12 R 13	15 F 13 / 15 RS 13	18 FCT 13 / 18 FCV 13

C = Side-hung F = Fixed light T = Top-hung S = Fixed sublight
V = Top-hung full width R = Horizontally pivoted

Typical details from Module 100 range

Fig. 12.1 Metal-window range

a slotted hole in the lug. The frame is fixed to the lug by means of self-tapping screws.

Metal windows are likely to expand at a greater rate than the surrounding concrete; provision must therefore be made to accommodate the thermal movement and at the same time maintain a weather seal. A flexible seating compound is therefore used together with a mastic seal (fig. 12.2).

12.2 Patent glazing

A patent-glazing system is the support of glass panes without the use of putty, for both vertical and inclined applications. Two forms of patent glazing are identified in BS 5516. The conventional type provides support along two edges of the glass and is usually found in sloping applications. The four-edge type, as the name implies, provides support to all four edges of a pane and is used vertically in side-wall systems where greater wind pressures are likely to occur.

There is a large range of proprietary systems on the market, but in general the system (fig. 12.3) consists of

117

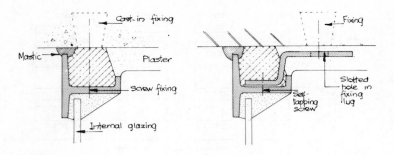

Fig. 12.2 Window fixing

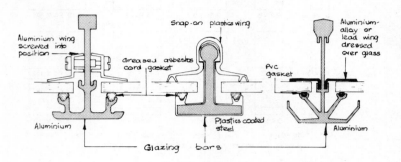

Fig. 12.3 Patent-glazing terminology

a) glazing bar — a metal T-shaped member which is the vertical inclined load-bearing element supporting the glass;

b) transom — a horizontal glazing bar;

c) wing or capping — anchored to the glazing bar or transom and providing a barrier to water penetration as well as securing the glass in position;

d) head — the horizontal member at the top of the system;

e) shoe — a fitting securing the glazing bar to the structure at its lower end;

f) stop — a fitting preventing the glass from sliding out of the lower end of the system;

g) gaskets — providing a draught and weather seal.

Glazing bars are manufactured in different stalk lengths to take account of the glass thickness and single or double glazing, and their sectional shape also incorporates condensation grooves and location grooves for gaskets. The bars are generally set at 600 mm centres, although larger distances may be achieved with heavier-duty profiles.

12.3 Patent-glazing details
Details of a typical aluminium patent-glazing system are shown in figs. 12.4 and 12.5.

118

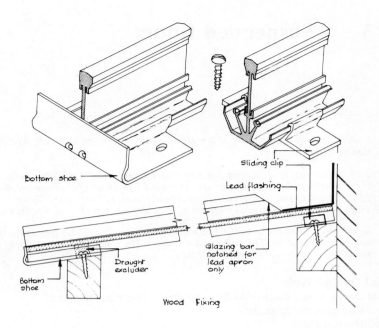

Bottom shoe

Sliding clip

Lead flashing

Draught
excluder

Bottom
shoe

Glazing bar
notched for
lead apron
only

Wood Fixing

Fig. 12.4 Patent-glazing details

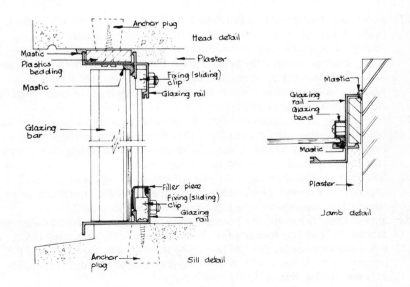

Anchor plug

Head detail

Mastic

Plaster

Plastics
bedding

Mastic

Fixing (sliding)
clip

Glazing rail

Glazing
bar

Mastic

Glazing
rail
Glazing
bead

Mastic

Filler piece

Fixing (sliding)
clip

Glazing
rail

Plaster

Jamb detail

Anchor
plug

Sill detail

Fig. 12.5 Patent-glazing details

119

13   Suspended floors

Understands the construction of precast r.c. suspended floors, including the formation of openings.

13.1 *States that load-carrying capacity, fire resistance, sound insulation, self-weight, and economic span are the basic design criteria for suspended floors.*
13.2 *Describes and sketches details of typical precast r.c. suspended floors.*
13.3 *Sketches and describes methods of providing openings in concrete floors.*

Acknowledgement is due to the Technician Education Council for permission to use the content of the TEC units in this chapter. The council reserves the right to amend the content of its units at any time.

13.1 Design criteria
The design of any suspended floor is subject to the constrains of
a)   load-carrying capacity,
b)   fire resistance,
c)   sound insulation,
d)   self-weight,
e)   economic span.

a)   *Load-carrying capacity*   Most floors are designed using the principles of beam design, and these principles are that (i) the beam must be strong enough to resist the applied bending movements; (ii) the beam must be strong enough to resist the applied shear forces; and (iii) the beam must not deflect excessively in either the horizontal or vertical planes. These principles all depend to some extent on the strength of the beam material and its ability to carry load.

b)   *Fire resistance*   A suspended floor which will readily burn is a hazard not only to the goods and occupants of that floor but also to those on the floor immediately below. It may also cause a loss of stability to the overall structure as a result of the reduced bracing effect.

c)   *Sound insulation*   For suitable levels of comfort, the transmission of sound from one area of a building to another should be restricted; in this respect the floor has as big a role to play as the walls.

d)   *Self-weight*   It has already been stated in (a) above that the load-carrying capacity of a beam/floor is a factor in the design of a suspended floor, but the load to be carried has two components — the dead load and the imposed load. If the dead load (self-weight) is large, it reduces the amount of imposed load which the floor will carry.

e)   *Economic span*   In designing a beam or floor, the bending strength and deflection, (a) (i) and (a) (iii), together with the self-weight (d) all have a component of span involved. The designer must therefore combine these various aspects in order to achieve economy of material usage in a given situation.

13.2 Precast concrete floors

The object of incorporating a precast concrete floor into a building is to effect economy of construction, and this is achieved by the use of standard units which both eliminate much of the temporary support works associated with in-situ construction and also reduce the duration of these operations.

This form of floor construction falls into one of two categories: either self-centring or partially self-centring. *Self-centring* is the term applied to a floor which does not require temporary soffit support (centring) either during or after construction.

The floor units may be either precast with ordinary reinforcing bars or prestressed. The prestressed units provide either increased span, reduced depth, or higher load-carrying capacity than the comparable reinforced-concrete units.

a) *Partially precast beam and filler block* Figure 13.1(a) shows a partially precast concrete beam which has reinforcement projecting from the top surface. The beams support a lightweight concrete or clay filler block. An in-situ concrete topping is poured over the beams and blocks to provide a monolithic construction. An upper layer of reinforcement may be added, as required by design, and service ducts may be located prior to pouring the topping. This system is suitable for spans up to 12 m but requires temporary propping during construction and a subsequent ceiling finish.

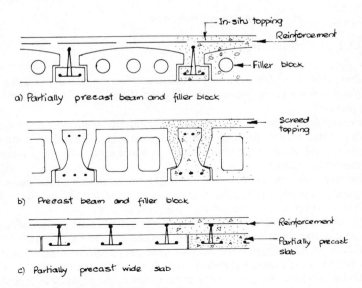

a) Partially precast beam and filler block

b) Precast beam and filler block

c) Partially precast wide slab

Fig. 13.1 Precast beam and filler block

121

b) *Precast beam and filler block* Similar to (a) above but the beam is fully precast and may be ordinarily reinforced or prestressed. Beams span up to 12 m.

c) *Partially precast wide slab* Again similar to (a), but not having any filler blocks, the precast portion is cast on a glass-fibre sheet to produce a smooth self-finish soffit requiring only a decorative finish. Slabs span up to 5 m.

d) *Precast plank* Suitable for lightly loaded floors or roofs, the prestressed units require only grouted joints and a screed topping, their main advantages being in their relatively small depth of construction and not requiring any centring (fig. 13.2).

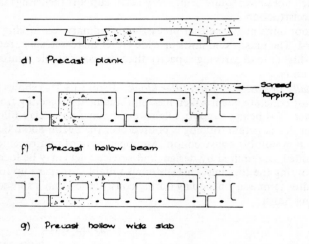

d) Precast plank

f) Precast hollow beam

g) Precast hollow wide slab

Fig. 13.2 Precast flooring

e) *Precast hollow plank* A deeper construction than (d), above using lightweight concrete, provides relatively good thermal insulation for short-span roofs.

f) *Precast hollow beams* These may be ordinarily reinforced or prestressed, depending on the span and loading requirements. The hollow centre section creates a weight reduction as well as a facility to run services through the units.

g) *Precast hollow wide slab* Similar to (f), the wide slab allows increased speed of erection and reduced labour costs provided that access and heavy lifting equipment are available on site.

h) *Precast trough units* Again similar to (f) but allowing greater access for the incorporation of services within the trough (see fig. 13.3).

j) *Precast double-T units* An extension of the trough unit, these units have good load-carrying capacity over long spans and are suitable for use in locations where a ceiling finish is not required, such as industrial buildings or car parks.

122

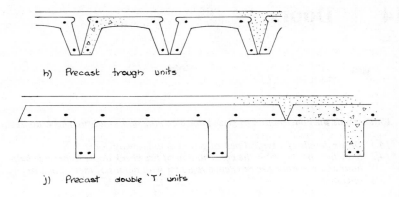

h) Precast trough units

j) Precast double 'T' units

Fig. 13.3 Trough units

13.3 Provision of openings

Openings are provided in floors for stairways, lifts, and services, and their location will generally be determined at an early stage of the building design, thus allowing special units incorporating holes for the smaller services to be precast. For the larger openings, a system of trimming around the opening similar to that used in suspended timber floors (see volume 1, chapter 13) is adopted. The trimming is carried out either by incorporating supporting units within the structural framework of the building or by casting an upstand or downstand in-situ reinforced-concrete ring beam around the opening integral with the precast units (fig. 13.4). This latter method will require temporary supports to be provided to the precast units in the vicinity of the opening.

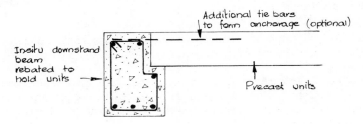

Fig. 13.4 Opening formation

14   Doors

Understands the construction of glazed double-swing doors and fire-check doors.

*14.1 Draws details of a typical pair of glazed double-swing doors.
*14.2 Sketches and describes the construction of fire-check doors to provide half-
hour and one-hour fire resistance together with details of their fixing to
openings.

Acknowledgement is due to the Technician Education Council for permission to
use the content of the TEC units in this chapter. The council reserves the right to
amend the content of its units at any time.

14.1 Glazed double-swing doors
These doors are frequently used in high-traffic areas, such as entrances and
corridors, to enable persons both to see and to be seen by other users.

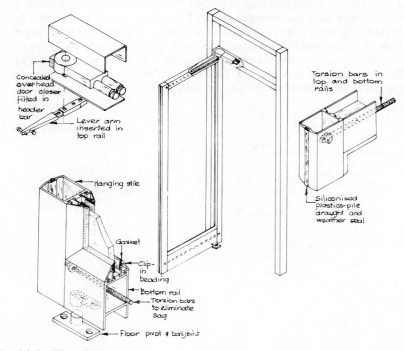

Fig. 14.1   Glazed doors

124

Because they are subject to heavy usage, they must be of strong construction (both framing and glass) as must be the hinging mechanism, which may be located in a variety of positions.

Weather and draught proofing is another important consideration where these doors are used in an external situation.

Figures 14.1 and 14.2 show typical details of construction.

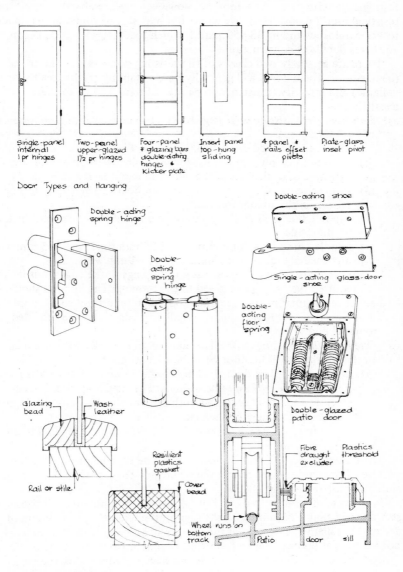

Fig. 14.2 Glazed doors

14.2 Fire-check doors

Fire-check doors are provided in a building to contain a fire within a given area (these areas being detailed in section E of the Building Regulations 1976). These doors must be able to resist the passage of fire for a period of time equal to that specified in Table 1 of the regulations and are deemed to be satisfactory if they meet the requirements of BS 476:part 8 in respect of testing. The term 'fire-check door' has now been replaced by the term 'fire-resisting door' in most legislative works but may still be found in manufacturers' catalogues and in BS 459:part 3, which together with BRE Digest 155 gives details of construction.

There are generally two classes of fire-resisting door: (a) half-hour and (b) one-hour. These doors will generally have a stability (resistance to collapse) and integrity (resistance to passage of flame) equal to their classification.

a) *Half-hour fire-resisting door* (fig. 14.3)   The constructional requirements of such a door are
   i)   minimum finished door thickness to be 44 mm;
   ii) a 3 mm thick plywood or hardboard facing to be glued over the full face area of both sides of the door (no metal facing to be used);
   iii) protective panels of 9 mm thick plasterboard to be fitted into 25 mm rebates in the timber framing;
   iv) top rail, bottom rail, and stiles to be a minimum of 38 mm thick and 95 mm wide;
   v)   middle rail to be a minimum size of 38 mm thick and 165 mm wide;
   vi) intermediate rails to be a minimum of 44 mm wide.

   Internal doors may be used without lippings to the edges, but if lippings are required they should be glued to the framing. The lippings should be either rectangular or tongued-and-grooved and must not show more than 9 mm on the door face. Lippings on all four edges must be provided for external doors.

b) *One-hour fire-resisting door*   The construction of this door is similar to that of the half-hour door with the exception of
   i)   minimum finished door thickness to be 54 mm – this results from a 5 mm thickness of asbestos wallboard or insulating board being glued to the full face area of both sides of the door (fig. 14.3), the board being applied in one piece;
   ii) where lippings are used, they must be tongued and glued into grooves in the rails and stiles.

The frames to fire-resisting doors must also be capable of resisting the passage of fire, and for this reason the rebate and stop must be large and of suitable construction (fig. 14.3).

In the case of a frame to a half-hour door, the minimum overall size of section is 55 mm × 83 mm, with the depth of rebate being a minimum of 25 mm. If a planted stop is used then it should be fixed with 38 mm long no. 8 screws at 600 mm centres, starting 75 mm in from each end.

The frame for a one-hour door may not have a planted stop, the rebate being formed from a solid piece of timber which should then be pressure-

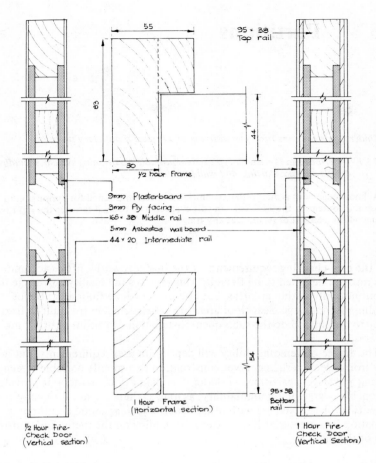

Fig. 14.3 Fire-check doors

impregnated with a fire-retardant solution.

The fitting of the door in its frame is also important for fire-resistance purposes, and there should be a maximum clearance of 3 mm between the door and frame. The hinges (1 pair for half-hour, $1\frac{1}{2}$ pairs for one-hour) should not be affected by the fire, hence plastics hinges are suspect. The locks must be of suitable size, taking account of the door frame sizes, and, since fire-resisting doors should be kept closed, self-closing mechanisms should also be fitted.

127

15   Partitions

Understands the construction and fixing of a typical proprietary partition.

*15.1 Describes and sketches a typical demountable partitioning system, including details at head, skirting, and wall junction.

Acknowledgement is due to the Technician Education Council for permission to use the content of the TEC units in this chapter. The council reserves the right to amend the content of its units at any time.

For the ever-changing requirements of the business world, office accommodation must be designed to be flexible. This requires the facility to change the layout not only within an office but also of the whole floor area. Hence buildings having large clear floor areas are constructed with a built-in flexibility to accommodate the subsequent installation of various partitioning systems.

The degree of demountability will depend on user requirements, but it may vary from a semi-permanent wet construction to a mobile portable screen or folding and sliding partitions or doors. The rigid dry constructions provide a reasonable degree of demountability, as long as there are not too many components involved, coupled with other benefits such as sound and thermal insulation to a greater or lesser extent, depending on the method of construction of the unit.

15.1 Demountable partitions
The majority of demountable partition systems consist of a framework and infill panelling.

a)   *Framework*   The framing members are made from either pressed steel, extruded aluminium, or hard or soft wood; and the frame may be either covered by the panel, exposed, or covered by a strip. The framing not only provides a support for the panelling but also acts as a locator for the partition at wall, ceiling, and floor. The hollow metal frames may also act as ducting for services such as electricity, telephones, and possibly water.

In order to reduce sound transmission through the structure, it is advisable to set the locating members on a foam-rubber sealing strip. Because the panels are of standard sizes, the fitting of such panels into both height and length situations which are not equal to or exact multiples of those standards has caused one of the major drawbacks of standard-unit systems. Developments in jointing techniques have to some

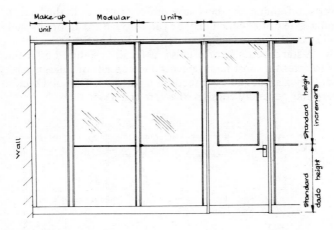

Fig. 15.1 Partition layout

extent overcome the problem by the use of a bellows or sliding joint, but there may still be a need for special or cut make-up pieces — see fig. 15.1.

In the construction shown in fig. 15.2, the framing consists of channel members screwed to the floor and wall with a top capping fixed to the ceiling soffit. Intermediate posts are formed between each panel by the framing or adjacent panels and a cover plate slotting in between them.

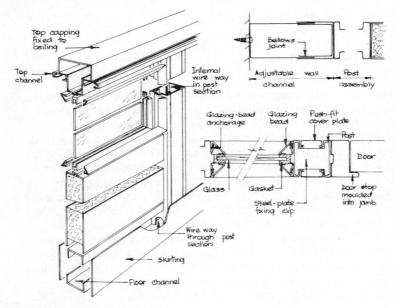

Fig. 15.2 Partition details

The vertical framing members have preformed holes in the base to accommodate cables which may be run through the floor channel section as well as up the posts to light-switches and other fittings.

b) *Panels* A standard range of panels is generally produced by manufacturers to cater for most requirements and consists of solid, partially glazed, fully glazed, and door sections (fig. 15.3). The solid section of the panelling generally consists of a core and a skin.

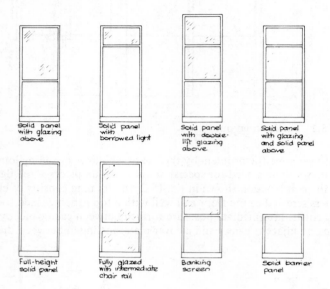

Fig. 15.3 Range of panels

The core may be honeycombed, strawboard, foamed plastics, timber lathing, glass-fibre quilt, mineral wool, or solid material such as chipboard or blockboard. The skin may be paper, cardboard, plastics laminates, plasterboard, or steel sheet, and the combination of core and skin is designed to suit market requirements in respect of durability, fire resistance, weight, decoration, and cost. The panels normally have an outer frame which provides additional rigidity as well as a means of fixing. The glazing is held in place by gaskets and removable beading.

In the construction shown in fig. 15.2, the panel is inserted into the top channel and then located in the bottom channel and subsequently anchored by self-tapping screws through the top channel into the panel. This fixing is covered by a push-fit capping channel. After completion of any service connections, the post-section cover plates are clipped into place and finally the skirting is fixed (fig. 15.4).

Door sections are delivered with the door prehung.

130

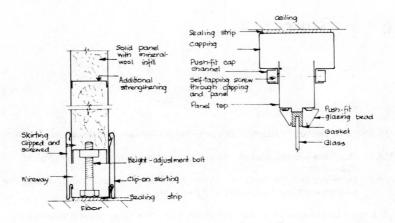

Fig. 15.4 Skirting detail

131

16   Stairs

Understands the construction of an open-riser timber stair and an in-situ r.c. stair.

*16.1   Describes and sketches the construction of an open-riser timber straight-
flight stair.*

16.2   *Describes and sketches the construction of an r.c. in-situ stair, including the
positioning of reinforcement and formwork.*

Acknowledgement is due to the Technician Education Council for permission to use the content of the TEC units in this chapter. The council reserves the right to amend the content of its units at any time.

16.1 Open-riser stairs

An open-riser stair is one having no risers, just the treads and their support. This form of construction, while forming an interesting architectural feature, also facilitates a more even distribution of heat and light, as well as making cleaning easier. It has, however, been all but eliminated in domestic construction, since the 1976 Building Regulations, clause H3 (4) (j), require that if any flight forms part of a building or building compartment for residential purposes or an institutional building where children under 5 years old are likely to be present, there is to be no open rise or opening in a rise through which a 100 mm diameter sphere would pass. In such cases a half riser would have to be incorporated (fig. 16.1).

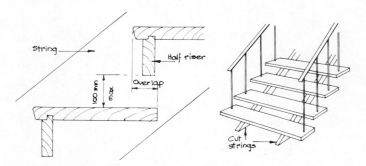

Fig. 16.1   Open-string stair

Since the soffit of the tread in an open-rise stair is not supported by a riser, the tread itself must be strengthened by increasing the thickness to a minimum of 38 mm, and for safety it is advisable that the nosing of each tread should overlap the tread below.

The most common methods of supporting the treads in this form of construction are

a) *Traditional strings* The construction is similar to that shown in volume 1, fig. 14.6, but without the risers and glue blocks.

b) *Cut strings* The 'cut string' provides a good appearance and may be formed in natural or laminated timber and steel.

c) *Single central spine or carriage* (fig. 16.2) The spine may be made of natural or laminated timber or rectangular hollow-section steel for support to timber treads or concrete in the case of precast concrete treads. In all cases both the tread and its connection to the spine must be strong enough to support the cantilever-loading effect of people climbing the stairs near the balustrade, as well as the loading imposed from the balustrade itself.

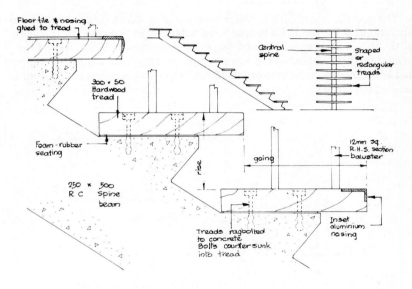

Fig. 16.2 Central-carriage stair

16.2 Reinforced-concrete stairs
Concrete stairs must conform to the same criteria for design as timber stairs, but the major advantage over timber is that of greater fire resistance.

For economy the concrete is reinforced and the stairs are designed to span either horizontally from a wall to a beam or longitudinally from floor to floor or landing to landing.

Stairs which span horizontally — see fig. 16.3 — are not often constructed since they require either a stringer beam and wall to provide support, which means expensive cutting in; or a break in brickwork continuity while stair construction proceeds; or two stringer beams, which are expensive luxuries.

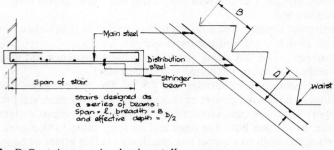

Fig. 16.3 R.C. stair spanning horizontally

The popular construction, which does not slow down other construction operations, is for the stairs to span longitudinally. In this case the thickness of the slab is the waist dimension (ideally a minimum of 100 mm) and the main steel is positioned in the soffit region, running from support to support and being incorporated into or linked with the reinforcement in the floor or landing (fig. 16.4).

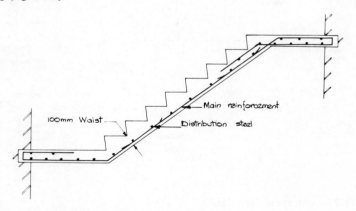

Fig. 16.4 R.C. stair spanning longitudinally

The formwork to the stairs (fig. 16.5) consists of a ply or board soffit shutter which is supported by means of bearers and ledgers, their layout being decided on site for convenience and ease of stripping. This soffit support is in turn supported by struts and bracing from the floor below. The landing formwork is constructed as if it were a small floor (see volume 2, chapter 8).

Because the stairs are in effect a sloping slab, a fairly stiff concrete mix is required if it is not to flow excessively, and this in turn means that access must be provided for both placing and compacting the concrete. Hence the

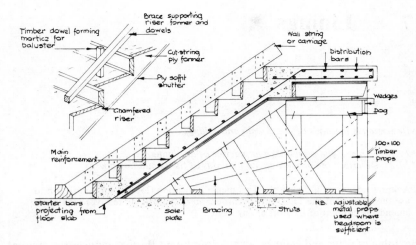

Fig. 16.5 Formwork to in-situ stair

tread is not created by formwork but is formed by hand trowelling. The riser is created by forms which are supported by a wallboard and hanger where the stairs abut a wall and by a cut string at the outer edge. Where there is a wide staircase, further support to the riser may be required to prevent bowing as a result of the concrete pressure, and this is provided by a central stiffener or brace. In order to facilitate stripping as well as to allow the whole of the tread to be trowelled, the bottom of the riser former is chamfered.

Provision for the fixing of balusters may be incorporated during casting by the insertion of boxes or fixings, but it is easier and more accurate to drill out holes for fixings after casting but while the concrete is still 'green'.

17 Linings

Understands methods of lining walls and ceilings.

*17.1   Explains the principles and practice of dry lining.
*17.2   Describes the properties and methods of fixing building boards.

Acknowledgement is due to the Technician Education Council for permission to
use the content of the TEC units in this chapter. The council reserves the right to
amend the content of its units at any time.

The lining of walls and ceilings with various board finishes reduces the amount
of time spent on the finishing operations when compared to the traditional
'wet' plaster finishing, where each coat must be allowed to harden before the
application of a further coat and the whole finish must be allowed to dry out
prior to decoration.

17.1 Dry lining

The term 'dry lining' relates specifically to the use of taper-edged plasterboard sheets fixed to a wall on battens or by plaster dabs. This method provides a quick and dry form of construction — only the joint finish (see
volume 2, fig. 13.4) is a wet operation and it dries very quickly — but it
requires a reasonably true wall surface to receive the fixing. The battens can
be either timber (approx. 40 mm × 10 to 15 mm in section) or strips of
plasterboard. The timber battens are fixed to the wall by nails fired from a
cartridge tool and, in cases where there is a likelihood of moisture presence
in the wall, the timber should be pressure-impregnated with preservative.
The plasterboard strips are fixed to the wall using special adhesive. Both
battens and strips can take up a certain amount of wall undulation and are
spaced to provide edge fixing for the boards, at a maximum of 450 mm
centres, the initial fixing being made at skirting and ceiling level to provide
a datum for all subsequent fixings.

The alternative fixing for the plasterboard is the plaster dab. This method
consists of bedding 75 mm × 50 mm thin bitumen-impregnated fibreboard
dots in board-finish plaster on the wall at approximately 1.0 m centres
vertically and 1.8 m centres horizontally. These dots are plumbed in all directions on the wall to provide a datum for subsequent infill dots which are
spaced at 450 mm centres. A couple of hours later, when the dots are set,
board-finish plaster is applied vertically to the wall between the dots, in short
sections some 100 mm apart, the sections or dabs being thicker than the dots
(fig. 17.1). The plasterboard sheets are pressed on to the dabs until they are
in contact with the dots, and they are then secured temporarily to the dots

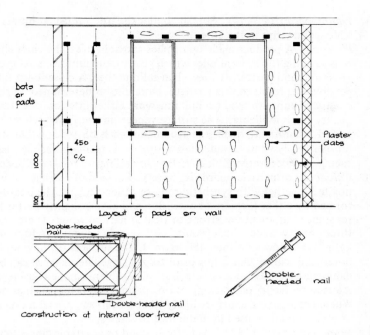

Dots or pads

450 c/c

1000

100

Layout of pads on wall

Double-headed nail

Plaster dabs

Double-headed nail

Double-headed nail

Construction at internal door frame

Fig. 17.1 Fixing plasterboard

with double-headed nails until the dabs have set. When the boards are secure, the nails are removed for reuse and the joints between sheets are made good.

Whichever method of fixing is used, the wall construction is completed and the boarding is ready to receive a decorative finish in hours rather than weeks. Additional benefits from this form of construction are that problems of efflorescence on the wall surface are eliminated; the additional cavity created between the board and the wall also improves thermal insulation, particularly if foil-backed plasterboard is used; and there is a plane surface finish which is unlikely to be subject to shrinkage cracking.

17.2 Building boards
There is a wide variety of building boards which may be used as linings for walls and ceilings, and their selection is based on appearance properties, cost, and, most important of all, compliance with the regulations relating to the spread of flame over the surface (Building Regulations 1976, section E15). They include
a) *Solid wood panelling* Very expensive and nowadays found only in older buildings or specialist situations where the lining might also form part of the structure.
b) *Blockboard* (BS 3444) Consists of a core of thin 25 mm wide wood strips bonded together to form a slab and faced with veneer or ply. It has similar properties to the solid wood but is much cheaper.

137

c) *Laminboard* (BS 3444)   Similar to blockboard, but using thinner 7 mm wide wood strips in the core.

d) *Plywood*   A product made up of plies and adhesives, the chief characteristic being the crossed plies which give a more uniform strength in all directions and greater stiffness than solid timber. A closer edge fixing is possible as a result of this strength. Durability is determined by the quality of adhesive used (in building work either interior- or exterior-quality ply is available). The surface veneer finish of the plywood is also graded according to quality in accordance with BS 1455. Other surface finishes to plywood include 'decorative' veneers, metal facing, plastics facing, and decorative film covering (sometimes termed 'wallboard').

e) *Chipboard* or particle board (BS 5669)   Consists of particles of wood bonded together with synthetic resin or other binders. The boards are formed by either pressure or extrusion and have a slightly better fire resistance but are not as strong or rigid as natural wood. There are three density grades: high (800 to 640 kg/m^3), medium (640 to 480 kg/m^3), and low (less than 480 kg/m^3). The surfaces of the boards are pitted and will require filling prior to painting. The material can be damaged by excessive moisture, but this problem can be considerably reduced by facing veneers or surface coatings of plastics such as melamine. Where heavy fixing loads are likely to be sustained, special fixing clips or plugs should be used in preference to screws.

f) *Fibre boards* (BS 1142)   Made from wood or vegetable fibres felted together during the rolling or pressing of the board from pulp. There are three main varieties:

    i) Hardboard — made under high pressure, provides a hard smooth surface on one side and a mesh texture on the other. Further treatment with oils and heat produces a tempered hardboard which has more strength and moisture resistance than a normal hardboard and is recognised by its darker brown colouring. Hardboards may have a variety of finishes including veneer, p.v.c. sheet, enamelling, moulding, embossing, impregnated flame-retardant, or printed wood-grain. A major advantage is that the board can be formed into curves as small as 300 mm radius, without special treatment.

    ii) Medium boards — of high (HM) or low (LM) density having a matt, silky, or hard shiny surface. Can be used for notice boards.

    iii) Insulation boards — lightly compressed and having a textured surface. They provide good thermal insulation and sound absorption, but have a high rate of flame spread which may be reduced by impregnation or a surface coating of emulsion paint.

g) *Wood-wool slabs* (BS 1105)   Made by compressing wood shavings coated with cement. They have a low rate of flame spread and their open texture provides good sound absorption and thermal insulation.

Most building boards should be conditioned before fixing, and this means that they should be stored initially in a cool dry place on a flat surface with their edges protected. Before they are incorporated in the building, all wet trade work should have been completed and the building should be completely weather-sealed. The boards should be stacked in the room for at least 48 hours prior to fixing, to allow for adjustment in the moisture content.

The boards are fixed to a timber-batten framework similar to that for the dry-lining process, the amount of support between the edges of the board being dictated by the strength and thickness of the particular board. The method of fixing may be either by screwing, nailing, stapling, or adhesives, but in all cases it is good practice on wall lining to work from the top centre outwards and downwards, leaving the perimeter fixing until last; the sequence is similar for ceiling fixing (see fig. 17.2).

There are many methods of forming the joints between boards, depending upon the decorative effect required. Figure 17.3 shows some of the methods which may be used.

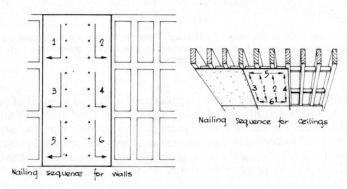

Fig. 17.2 Board fixing

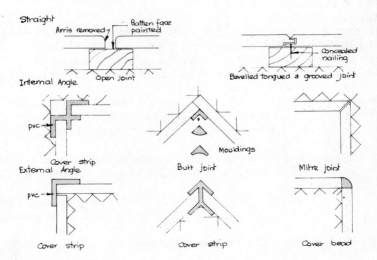

Fig. 17.3 Board jointing

139

18   Paintwork

Identifies common causes of paint failure.

18.1   Identifies the main defects found in painted finishes.
18.2   Explains reasons for these defects.
18.3   Explains methods of reducing the incidence of these defects.
18.4   Explains the importance of adequate preparation before applying paint finishes.

Acknowledgement is due to the Technician Education Council for permission to use the content of the TEC units in this chapter. The council reserves the right to amend the content of its units at any time.

The breakdown of any paint system, applied to a surface as a means of protection, will have a detrimental effect on that surface. The failure to fulfil the specific functions, e.g. loss of surface protection to a timber window sill, will result in far higher maintenance or replacement costs; hence by frequent inspection the recognition and treatment of painting defects can contribute to financial savings by preventive maintenance.

18.1 Main defects
The main defects are
a)   *Bittiness* — specks or small blotches on an otherwise smooth surface.
b)   *Bleeding* — discolouration of paint film — generally brownish.
c)   *Blistering* — visible bubbles under the surface of the paint film.
d)   *Blooming* — misty or hazy appearance on the surface of a gloss finish.
e)   *Chalking* — whitening of the surface of oil paints.
f)   *Cissing* (pinholing) — small depressions or holes in the paint film.
g)   *Crazing* — fine irregular cracks in the paint film.
h)   *Curtaining* (running, sagging) — film tends to sag in festoons or form unsightly runs.
j)   *Efflorescence* — white crystalline deposits formed on the surface of the paint film in the case of emulsion paints or under the film in the case of oil paints.
k)   *Flaking* (peeling) — paint film lifting or peeling away from the surface.
l)   *Grinning* (opacity) — failure to obliterate the colour of the previous surface.
m) *Mould growth* — greyish or sooty spotting or mould growth on the surface of the paint film.
n)   *Saponification* — soft, sticky, or soapy texture.

p) *Staining* (discolouration) — change of colour of surface, either as a change of shade or as colour alteration.

q) *Wrinkling* — small hard pointed ridges on the paint surface.

18.2 Causes

a) *Bittiness* A general lack of cleanliness in the whole painting operation — initially through not cleaning and dusting off the surface and subsequently from particles of broken paint skins and/or using dirty brushes and containers.

b) *Bleeding* Bitumen, creosote, nicotine, and other surface stains, together with resinous deposits exuding from knots in timber, strike through the new paint film since they are soluble in the paint medium.

c) *Blistering* Lack of adhesion between paint and surface. This may be due to (i) the presence of moisture between surface and paint film, (ii) the generation of gases between paint films or film and surface. Cause (i) is usually associated with woodwork or other porous materials which absorb and retain moisture in their cell structure; it may also occur as a result of painting being carried out in wet, damp, or foggy conditions where the surface has not been thoroughly dried prior to paint application. Cause (ii) may be the result of chemical action of driers, pigments, or resinous bleeding from knots in timber.

d) *Blooming* The presence of moisture during the application of the gloss coat or a chilling of the surface being glossed.

e) *Chalking* Powdering of the paint surface caused by external exposure to harmful chemicals and a breakdown of the paint binder.

f) *Cissing* Resulting from a loss of adhesion of the paint film, it occurs as a result of (i) varnishing over an old varnished surface without rubbing down properly, (ii) applying a finish coat to an undercoat after a long time lapse, thus the undercoat is so hard that it is impervious to the finish coat, (iii) insufficient cleansing of a greasy surface.

g) *Crazing* The loss of elasticity of the whole system, resulting from old age, the application of a film on to an undercoat which has not fully dried, or the application of a hard-drying film to a soft or oily undercoat.

h) *Curtaining* The use of incorrect brushing techniques whereby the paint is applied too heavily or unevenly, or a wet edge is left too long before continuation so that perfect merging cannot be achieved.

j) *Efflorescence* Water-soluble salts within the building fabric brought to the surface as a result of the fabric drying out.

k) *Flaking* A loss of adhesion between paint film and surface, allied to blistering where the moisture is brought to the surface by heat causing the paint film to lift away. Careless preparation of the surface by poor cleaning down, e.g. the leaving of loose particles of rust or dirt or the inadequate removal of old perished paint, also leads to flaking, as does the application of coats of emulsion paint over a number of years to a surface which is subject to constant expansion and contraction.

l) *Grinning* The application of too thin a film on to a previous coat of vastly different colour.

m) *Mould growth* Mould growth develops under damp or humid conditions where cultures or organic matter are readily available, such as in kitchens, breweries, dairies, and bakeries. Damp plaster, timber, and wallpaper also promote mould growth.

n) *Saponificàtion* Alkaline attack of the paint – plaster and cement surfaces have a high alkali content.

p) *Staining* Outside agents reacting with the various paint constituents may cause this problem, but more commonly it is the result of the natural ageing of the paint film.

q) *Wrinkling* Occurs in varnishes and gloss paint where there is too thick an application of the film to the undercoat. It happens more frequently in hot weather where the surface drying is accelerated, leaving a comparatively soft underfilm to which oxygen cannot penetrate in order to complete the drying process. Subsequently, movement of the underfilm will cause the dry top surface to wrinkle.

18.3 Remedies

In certain cases the above-mentioned defects may be remedied by sanding down and repainting. In the majority of cases the defect is best avoided by adopting proper working procedures and techniques.

a) *Bittiness* Rub down the surface with glass paper to obtain a smooth surface; ensure the surface is both clean and dry; use clean equipment and fresh paint.

b) *Bleeding* Strip off the affected paint and, if possible, remove the cause of the defect. Where removal is impossible the surface should be sealed with a suitable sealer (in the case of knots a shellac knotting should be used) prior to repainting.

c) *Blistering* Remove all the defective paint and ensure that the surfaces are dry before applying paint. The use of a suitable primer will assist in obtaining good adhesion between the paint system and the original surface.

d) *Blooming* Remove with a soft rag or wash down with clean water, polish, or rub down with fine glass-paper and regloss.

e) *Chalking* Wash with clean water, rub down, seal, and repaint.

f) *Cissing* May be avoided by vigorous brushing where the problem is experienced during application of the paint film. Alternatively, a newly applied coat should be immediately washed off with white spirit and be allowed to dry; the surface is then rubbed down with abrasive paper or pumice and refinished. The latter treatment is also used for surfaces that have already hardened.

g) *Crazing* Strip the surface and repaint using compatible materials, allowing sufficient drying time between the application of each film.

h) *Curtaining* Avoided by brushing the paint well out using cross-brushing techniques and an even thin application of paint. The remedy is to rub down the runs and curtains until they are smooth with the surrounding surface and then repaint.

j) *Efflorescence* The salt deposits should be thoroughly brushed from the surface, and no attempt should be made to seal them in or wash them off. An emulsion paint may be applied to the surface (being porous, this will allow the salts to crystallise on the paint surface rather than underneath). Other forms of painting should not be attempted until the building fabric is completely dried out, this being indicated by the cessation of this particular problem.

k) *Flaking* Avoided by good preparation work and application of the paint system to a dry surface. The remedy is to remove all the paint and start again from a bare surface. Where complete removal of the paint is difficult (water-thinned paints pose a particular problem), all loose paint should be scraped off and the whole area be bound by a good coating of oil primer before rebuilding the subsequent paint system.

l) *Grinning* Avoided by the use of suitable coloured undercoat(s) and gloss coat. The problem may be remedied by further applications of paint film until complete obliteration is achieved.

m) *Mould growth* Avoided by removing the cause of the dampness, either within the building fabric or by adequate ventilation of the atmosphere, and then washing down with an antiseptic solution. The remedy is to strip the paint and sterilise the surface with antiseptic solution prior to repainting with a fungicidal paint.

n) *Saponification* Avoided by the surfaces being thoroughly dry and coated with an alkali-resistant primer prior to normal painting. The remedy is to remove the defective work and treat the surfaces as above.

p) *Staining* May be avoided by frequent washing down of the surface using clean water. Repainting on the existing surface will overcome the problem provided that the surface is well rubbed down, washed off, and dry before application of the system.

q) *Wrinkling* Avoided by using thin films of paint to cover the surface and not applying the film on a hot day in direct sunlight. Remedied by removing the offending layer(s) and repainting.

18.4 Preparation

As can be seen from the foregoing sections, good workmanship embodying adequate preparation of the surface to be painted will greatly reduce the incidence of paint failure.

This preparation begins with an examination of the surface to be painted and an appreciation of the problems which may occur (those problems being items (b), (c), (d), (f), (j), (k), (l), (m), (n), and (p) listed in section 18.2).

The correct treatment of the surface, in terms of cleaning and rubbing down, must be carried out if subsequent failure or poor appearance of the paint system is to be avoided (items (a), (f), (j), and (k)).

The use of good-quality materials and equipment together with the correct application techniques is essential if a long film life and overall cost reduction are to be achieved (items (a), (e), (f), (g), (h), (l), and (q)).

It is obvious therefore, that good preparation is the key to good painting.

143

19   Heating systems

Understands the principles of typical domestic heating systems.

*19.1 Sketches and describes one- and two-pipe small-bore heating systems, indicating positions of component parts.
*19.2 Describes methods of controlling temperature and flow within these systems.

Acknowledgement is due to the Technician Education Council for permission to use the content of the TEC units in this chapter. The council reserves the right to amend the content of its units at any time.

19.1 Small-bore systems

In domestic premises the pipework supplying water to radiators may be small-bore (22 or 15 mm diameter) or microbore (6, 8, or 10 mm diameter). The correct sizing of the pipework is important for providing a given size of radiator with the required amount of heat, and the radiator size is based on the amount of heat-energy input required to combat the heat losses in a given room or location and the temperature at which a radiator will operate.

There are two main methods of supplying the hot water to the radiators:

a)   *One-pipe* or *single-pipe* system (fig. 19.1)   The hot water from the boiler is fed to each radiator on the circuit in turn, with the cooler water exiting from the radiator being fed back into the same pipe. Consequently the temperature of the water entering successive radiators is gradually reduced, and the control of heat distribution is therefore difficult. The only advantage of this system is the low cost and the ease of installation.

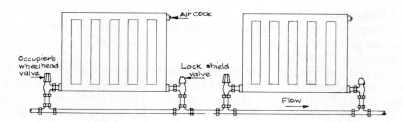

Fig. 19.1   One-pipe heating system

b)   *Two-pipe* system (fig. 19.2)   The hot water from the boiler is fed to each radiator by one pipe and the cooled water exiting from the radiators is collected by a second pipe and returned to the boiler.

144

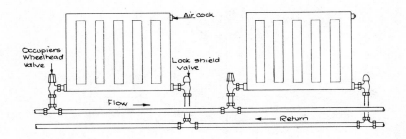

Fig. 19.2 Two-pipe heating system

The majority of domestic small-bore heating systems are operated in conjunction with an indirect hot-water supply system (volume 2, chapter 20), with connections being made to the primary flow and return circuits or by separate connections to the boiler unit.

The layout of the pipework circuits depends on the layout of the rooms on the various floor levels and the location of the radiators within those rooms. Radiators are generally located under windows in order to nullify the heat losses through windows. Typical schematic layouts of a one-pipe and a two-pipe system for a domestic property are shown in figs 19.3 and 19.4. For larger buildings with repetitive floor layouts, a drop system or ladder system may be used (fig. 19.5).

19.2 Controls

An efficient system of control is essential if an economic and comfortable level of heating within a property is to be achieved. The control of temperature and flow are interlinked, since a reduction in the flow of hot water through the system will reduce the heat emission and therefore the temperature.

The controls in common use are as follows.

a) *Circulating pump* Set on the return pipe prior to the boiler, it ensures that the flow of hot water in the circuit is sufficient to reach all radiators.

b) *Radiator valves* Each radiator is fitted with two valves:
   i) a wheel valve, which is adjusted by hand to increase, reduce, or shut off the supply of hot water to the radiator on the flow side;
   ii) a lock shield valve – a preset valve on the return side of the radiator which is used to balance the amount of heat provided to each radiator.

c) *Thermostatic valves* These may replace the radiator wheel valve so that individual room-temperature control may be provided.

d) *Air cock* Inserted in the top of a radiator to allow air, which would otherwise prevent water from entering the radiator, to be vented.

e) *Gate valves* Provide a facility to shut off a section of the system (one should be placed at each side of the pump, to allow its removal without draining off the whole system).

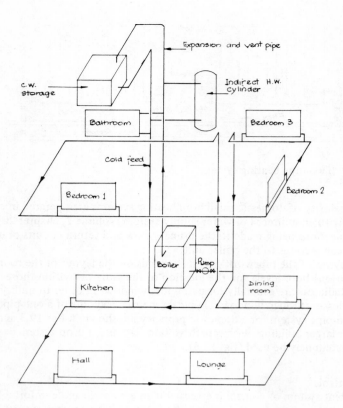

Fig. 19.3 Typical one-pipe layout

f) *Boiler thermostat*   This controls the temperature of the water in the boiler, either by controlling the rate at which fuel is burnt or by switching the boiler on and off.

g) *Room thermostat*   Located in the main living room away from draughts and fixed on a wall, approximately 1.5 m above floor level, this is set to the required room temperature and electrically controls the circulating pump.

h) *Frost thermostat*   Wired to over-ride other controls, this thermostat, which is similar to a room thermostat, is designed to switch on when the temperature falls very low. It is used only where parts of the system are susceptible to freezing.

j) *Programme control/time switch*   Controls the electricity supply to the whole system and dictates the sequence and duration of the various operations. It is usually located near the boiler.

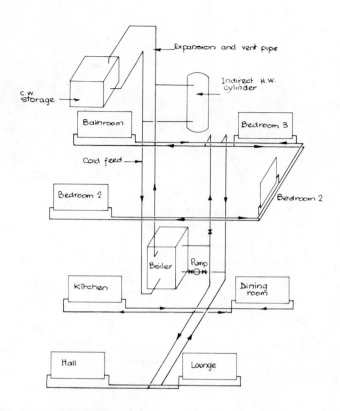

Fig. 19.4 Typical two-pipe layout

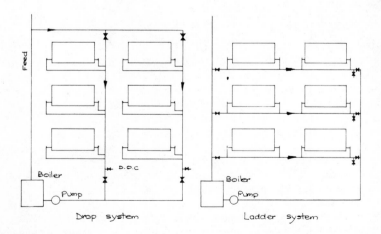

Fig. 19.5 Drops and ladders

147

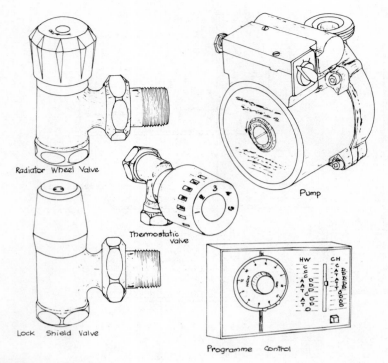

Radiator Wheel Valve

Thermostatic valve

Pump

Lock Shield Valve

Programme Control

Fig. 19.6 Controls

20   Electrical services

Understands the principles of a typical single-phase domestic electrical installation.

20.1   Identifies the items of equipment and space required by the Electricity Board at the intake position.
20.2   Identifies the need for correct cable sizing and the protection of circuits.
20.3   Identifies the consumer's control gear required at the intake position.
20.4   Identifies the electrical accessories used in typical domestic installations.
20.5   Identifies the main types of cable used in a domestic electrical installation.
20.6   Explains the principles of the ring-main wiring system.
20.7   Sketches and explains a typical domestic electrical installation including power and lighting circuits.

Acknowledgement is due to the Technician Education Council for permission to use the content of the TEC units in this chapter. The council reserves the right to amend the content of its units at any time.

20.1 Electricity Board equipment

The Electricity Board equipment provided at the intake position (fig. 20.1) consists of

a)   the *meter*, which records the amount of electricity consumed in kilowatt-hour (kW h) units;

b)   the *service fuse*, which is rated to cut off the supply if the load demand is in excess of the service-cable rating;

c)   an *earth connection* to which the house-circuit earth conductors are attached and from which a conductor is run to earth. In older properties this 'earth' was provided by the incoming water service pipe, but in more modern properties a separate earth electrode in the form of a long metal rod was driven into the ground outside the property and was connected to the earth terminal. Modern methods utilise the metal sheathing of the electricity service cable to provide the earthing facility.

    The space required to accommodate the above equipment is approximately 300 mm × 300 mm × 100 mm, but it is common practice to locate the consumer's control and distribution equipment in the same area, in many instances on a board subsequently fixed to a wall. The size of the board will vary from Board to Board, but a typical size would be 650 mm × 650 mm. The siting of the equipment must fulfil the following requirements:

   i)   ease of bringing the service cable to the controls,

  ii)   ease of bringing distribution cables to the controls,

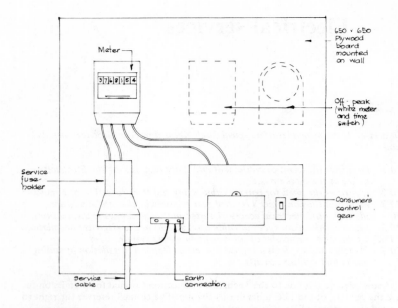

Fig. 20.1 Electricity Board equipment details

iii) ease of meter reading and accessibility,
iv) ease of maintenance,
 v) low risk of condensation,
vi) separation from the gas meter by a fire-resisting partition (in the case of a gas meter and electricity meter being housed in the same cupboard).

In many modern properties the above conditions are satisfied by a glass-fibre or plastics cabinet with a lockable door incorporated in the external leaf of a cavity wall (fig. 20.2).

20.2 Cable sizing

The amount of current which an electrical conductor or cable is able to carry is restricted by the effect of the heat which will be generated as a result of the conductor's resistance to the flow of the current. The temperature must be kept below the level at which a fire could be started or surrounding materials would be adversely affected.

The Institution of Electrical Engineers (IEE) in its regulations also states that the drop in voltage along any given conductor must not exceed 2.5 per cent of the nominal voltage when a conductor is carrying the maximum current.

Other factors which may affect the selection of conductor size are
  i) the type of protection from excess current afforded to the circuit,
 ii) the ambient temperature in the vicinity of the conductor,
iii) the proximity of other cables which might induce a heat build up.

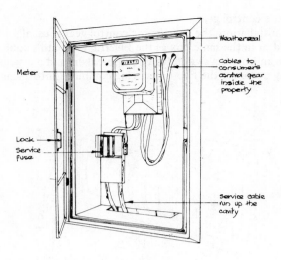

Fig. 20.2 External meter cabinet

Circuit protection

There are two classifications of circuit protection: close and coarse.

Close protection is provided by circuit breakers or certain types of cartridge fuse, both of which provide a very good protection from overload.

Coarse protection is provided by 'slow-acting' cartridge fuses and the rewirable forms of fuse carrier, fuse wire being relatively thin and designed to melt when too much current passes through it (fig. 20.3).

In both cases the object of the protection is rapidly to cut off the supply of current in the circuit before too much damage can occur.

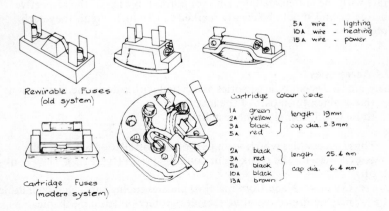

Fig. 20.3 Fuses

20.3 Consumer's control gear

In a domestic installation, the consumer's control gear is usually located on the same board or in the same box as the Electricity Board's equipment. The gear comprises an isolating switch (or circuit breaker) and a distribution fuse-board, in many instances the two units being combined into a single unit (fig. 20.4).

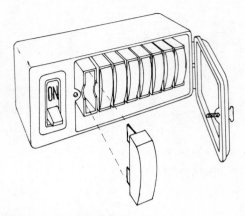

Fig. 20.4   Domestic consumer's control box

The *isolating switch* is the consumer's control of all the electricity entering the property and should be switched off before any electrical work is begun within the property, particularly work at the distribution fuse-board.

The *distribution fuse-board* contains a number of fuse carriers which protect the various subcircuits within the property, i.e. lighting, ring main, cooker, shower, etc. The fuses should have a rating (in amperes) commensurate with the anticipated demand for current in each of the respective subcircuits, and should be clearly marked as to which circuit they each protect.

20.4 Accessories

There are two types of accessories associated with a domestic installation:
a)   those which form part of the installation,
b)   those which complete the installation.

a)   Those accessories which form part of the installation are generally associated with the trunking or conduit system (fig. 20.5). They consist of
   i) *Conduit*   Made from metal or plastics tubing through which cables may be drawn, conduit provides protection from mechanical damage and allows rewiring with minimal damage to finishes. There are

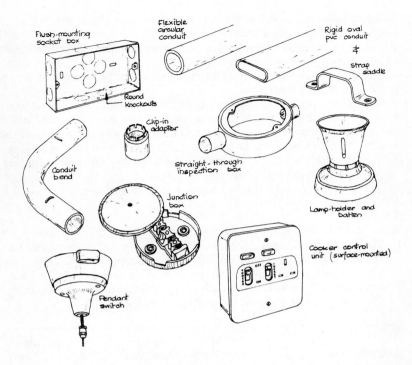

Fig. 20.5 Accessories

several forms of metal conduit, namely steel, aluminium, and copper, while the plastics variety is made of p.v.c.

  ii) *Conduit connectors*   Permit jointing of straight lengths of conduit.
 iii) *Conduit bends*   May have an access facility when the bend is sharp.
  iv) *Conduit boxes*   Facilitate drawing and jointing of cables and may have a number of outlets.
   v) *Insertion pieces*   Used to extend outlets or boxes to subsequent finished-surface level.
  vi) *Switch boxes*   House flush-mounted socket outlets or switches.
 vii) *Fixing clips, spacers, and saddles*   For positioning and anchoring conduit.
viii) *Channel*   Either metal or plastics – protects a cable when it is not in conduit.

b)   Those accessories which complete the installation are usually made from incombustible plastics which also provide insulation. They consist of

   i) *Switches*   May be single- or multiple-pole and also either one- or two-way.
  ii) *Pendant switch*   Used for ceiling mounting and operated by pulling a cord.
 iii) *Dimmers*   Reduce the lighting level without switching off.

iv) *Ceiling roses* Allow the lighting cable to hang from the ceiling while providing a suitable finish.

v) *Lamp-holders* Have various methods of holding the lamp bulb, e.g. bayonet or screw fittings.

vi) *Lamps* Are generally of a tungsten-filament or fluorescent type in domestic properties.

vii) *Socket outlets* Now standardised on three-pin (live, neutral, and earth) outlets. The outlets may be flush or surface-mounted and incorporate one or a number of outlet points or associated switches.

viii) *Plugs* Should now be of one size, the amount of current passing through the unit being restricted by a suitably rated cartridge fuse incorporated within the plug.

ix) *Junction boxes* Used to connect spurs to a circuit.

20.5 Cables

Cables have two main components: (a) conductors and (b) insulation.

a) The *conductor* is the metal wire or strand which carries the current and, in the majority of domestic cables, is made of copper. These conductors are classified by the number and diameter of the wires, e.g. 7/0.85 is a conductor having seven wires each of 0.85 mm diameter. Typical cable sizes for circuits are shown in fig. 20.6.

Application	Rating (amperes)	Cross-sectional area (mm^2)	No. and dia. of wires (mm)
Lighting circuits	11	1.0	1/1.13
Immersion heaters	13	1.5	1/1.38
Ring mains	18	2.5	1/1.78
	24	4.0	7/0.85
Cooker circuit	40	10.0	7/1.35

Fig. 20.6 Typical sizes of conductors

b) The *insulation* around the conductor prevents the leakage of current from the conductor. There are several types of insulation, but the two main varieties used in a domestic installation are

i) All-insulated sheathing – manufactured with one, two, or three insulated conductors. In the two-conductor (live and neutral) type, each conductor is separately insulated with coloured p.v.c. and the cable is subsequently formed by a p.v.c. sheath. The three-conductor cable contains a third conductor (earth), which may or may not be separately insulated (fig. 20.7). The colour coding for conductors is brown – live; blue – neutral; green and yellow – earth. Older circuits may be encountered in which the colour coding is red – live; black – neutral; green – earth.

154

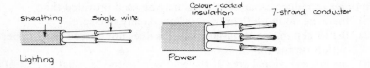

Fig. 20.7 Insulated cables

ii) Tough-rubber-sheathed (TRS) — similar to the all-insulated variety, but the conductors are insulated and sheathed with rubber. These cables are more flexible but do not have the same resistance to degradation with age.

20.6 The ring-main system
Strictly speaking, the ring main should be termed a ring circuit. This circuit begins from the distribution fuse-board, loops into the terminals of socket outlets, and returns to the same point on the distribution fuse-board.

The object of this circuit is to prevent overload, since any outlet on the circuit may be fed from two directions. This allows smaller conductor sizes to be used on the circuit, thereby reducing costs, while supplying a number of outlets. The fuse rating at the distribution board should be 30 amperes.

The regulations governing the design of a ring circuit vary between domestic and commercial installations. In the case of a domestic power installation, the following criteria should be observed.
a)   The circuit is to be wired using minimum 2.5 mm² all-insulated cables.
b)   The maximum floor area that may be served by a ring circuit is 100 m² — there being no restriction as to the number of socket outlets on the ring.

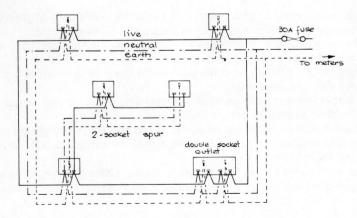

Fig. 20.8   Ring circuit

155

c) In order to reduce cable runs, spurs may be used provided that
   i) there are no more than two sockets on any one spur,
   ii) the total number of outlets on spurs does not exceed the number of outlets on the ring,
   iii) the cross-sectional area of the spur conductors is equal to that of the ring, unless it is separately fused.

A typical ring circuit is shown in fig. 20.8.

20.7 Layouts

The various electrical points should be located to suit the requirements of the individual occupiers, but in practice constraints in the form of cost and standardisation determine their locations. Figure 20.9 indicates the number of socket outlets which it is desirable to have in the various rooms of a domestic dwelling.

Location	Desirable number of socket outlets (Parker–Morris report)
Living room	5
Kitchen	4
Double bedroom	3
Single bedroom	2
Dining room	2
Hall	1
Landing	1
Garage	1

Fig. 20.9   Socket-outlet location

In general there is no restriction as to the location of electrical points, but in bathrooms or shower rooms certain criteria should be observed:
a) the lamp in a light fitting should be completely enclosed and have no exposed metal fittings;
b) light switches should be either outside the room or mounted at high level with pull-cord operation;
c) other switches (e.g. an immersion-heater switch) should not be accessible to a person using the bath or shower;
d) there should be no socket outlets in the room with the exception of an electric shaver point, which must be effectively earthed and also comply with BS 3052.

Figure 20.10 shows a typical domestic circuit layout (the symbols used are in accordance with BS 1192 — see volume 1, fig. 3.8).

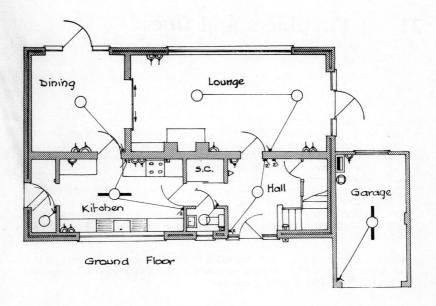

Ground Floor

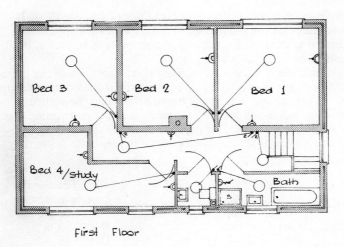

First Floor

Fig. 20.10 Circuit layout

21 Fireplaces and flues

Understands the principles of constructing flues for domestic heating appliances.

*21.1 Sketches and describes a typical ground-floor open fireplace, including junction with a suspended timber floor.
*21.2 Identifies methods of lining flues.
*21.3 Sketches and describes methods of providing underfloor ducted draught control to heating appliances.
*21.4 Identifies the principal types of gas fire and their flue requirements.
*21.5 Sketches and describes a typical flue-block installation, including various types of flue terminal.

Acknowledgement is due to the Technician Education Council for permission to use the content of the TEC units in this chapter. The council reserves the right to amend the content of its units at any time.

The construction of fireplaces and flues is governed by section L of the Building Regulations 1976, and British Standard Code of Practice CP 403 gives recommendations for the installation of domestic heating appliances. The accent is on the safety of the occupants of a property in respect of both fire and the emission of noxious fumes.

A fireplace must be designed so that its room's occupants obtain the maximum amount of heat, either directly by convection and radiation or indirectly by conduction and convection. For this to happen there must be sufficient air available for combustion and for efficient removal of the combustion gases. The design of the fireplace and the flue depends upon the appliance and the fuel it burns. Three classes of appliance are given in the regulations and they are:

Class	Rating (kW)	Fuel	Size of incinerator combustion chamber
High rating	Over 45 output	Solid or oil	Over 0.08 m^3
	Over 45 input	Gas	Over 0.08 m^3
Class 1	Under 45 output	Solid or oil	Between 0.03 m^3 and 0.08 m^3
Class 2	Under 45 input	Gas	Less than 0.03 m^3

21.1 Open fireplaces

Figure 21.1 indicates the terminology of the various components of an open fireplace.

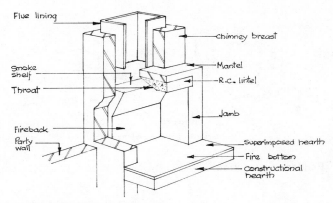

Fig. 21.1 Fireplace terminology

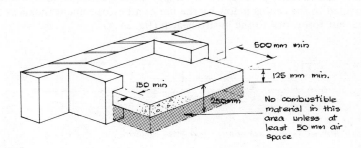

Fig. 21.2 Hearth regulations

a) The construction begins with the *constructional hearth* (fig. 21.2), for which the major requirements are that it should

   i) have a minimum thickness of 125 mm solid non-combustible material;

  ii) extend from the back of the fireplace recess and project a minimum of 500 mm in front of the jambs;

 iii) extend a minimum of 150 mm beyond either side of the jambs;

 iv) be constructed of such a size as to contain a square of 840 mm side, if there is no recess;

  v) have no combustible material placed underneath the hearth within 250 mm of the top surface unless there is a minimum separating air gap of 50 mm, or it provides support to the edge of the hearth.

    In the case of solid ground-floor or suspended concrete floor construction, the constructional hearth will normally form or be incorporated into such work. In a suspended timber ground-floor construction, the support is provided by hardcore and fender walls (fig. 21.3); while in upper-floor timber construction the hearth, either precast or more commonly in-situ,

159

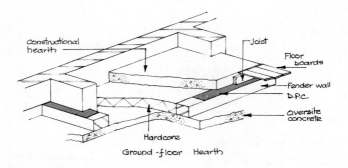

Ground-floor Hearth

Fig. 21.3 Fender construction

is supported by the chimney breast at the back and by fillets fixed to the trimmer and trimmer joists at the front and sides. Additional protection is provided to the ceiling below by the use of asbestos-cement sheets as permanent formwork to the in-situ hearth (fig. 21.4).

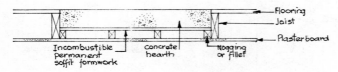

Section through Suspended Upper-floor Hearth

Fig. 21.4 Suspended-hearth construction

b) The fireplace *opening* should be 590 mm wide × 350 mm deep × (580 mm + 15 to 33 mm) height measured from finished hearth level to bottom lintel. These sizes are suitable for accommodating a fireback conforming to BS 1251 (fig. 21.5).

c) The *recesses*, which incorporate the jambs, shall have a thickness of not less than 200 mm of bricks, in-situ concrete, or concrete or clay blocks, with the exception of a cavity wall or an outside wall with no combustible cladding where respectively two 100 mm leaves or a single 100 mm leaf will satisfy the regulations (fig. 21.5).

d) The *lintel* supporting the brickwork over the opening should be of precast or in-situ reinforced concrete to BS 1251 (fig. 21.6).

e) The *fireback* may be of one, two, four, or six preformed pieces. Two or more pieces are preferable since, when jointed with asbestos rope, they reduce the risk of expansion cracking. Similarly, a layer of suitable material should act as a lining behind the fireback to allow for expansion between the fireback and the filling (fig. 21.7). Alternatively, where a

160

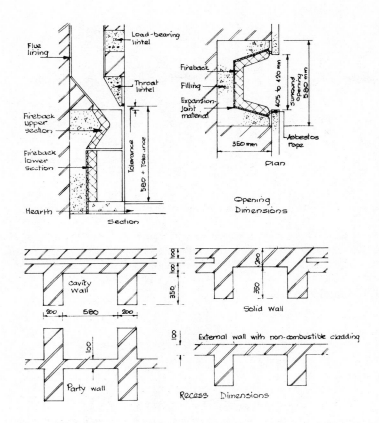

Section

Plan

Opening Dimensions

Cavity Wall

Solid Wall

Party wall

External wall with non-combustible cladding

Recess Dimensions

Fig. 21.5 Dimensions for recesses and openings

back-boiler is to be incorporated for water-heating purposes, a modified fireback is used incorporating a boiler unit, boiler flue, and flue damper control. Provision must be made in the recess to accommodate the hot-water flow and return pipes in sleeves, with the facility for draining the water from the system. The boiler unit is built in and tested before further work is continued, with the pipes sealed in their sleeves by asbestos-rope caulking.

f)   The *throat* may be formed in-situ or precast, giving a constant smooth opening size of approximately 100 mm × 250 mm (fig. 21.7); alternatively, an adjustable metal throat restrictor may be used. The object of the throat is to control the flow of air from the room into the flue aperture. The restriction increases the speed of the air which passes into the fireplace opening and which then carries the smoke from the fire into the flue.

g)   The *surround* is the finish to the fireplace and generally consists of a pre-cast ceramic tile slab or in-situ-built brick, slate, or stone. It is securely

161

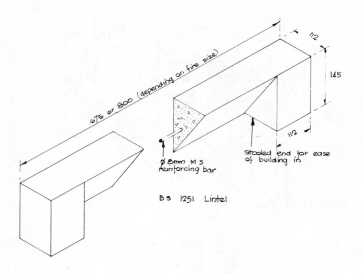

Fig. 21.6 Lintel detail

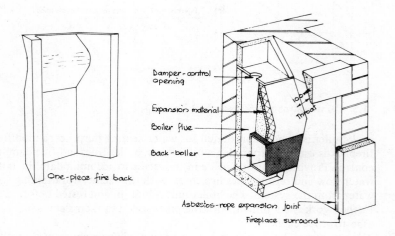

Fig. 21.7 Firebacks

fixed to the brickwork of the chimney breast by lugs cast in the back at each side of the surround. The hearth, similar in form to the surround, is bedded and levelled on the constructional hearth in a 1:1:6 cement:lime: sand mix. Both the hearth and the surround should also have provision for asbestos-rope expansion joints.

21.2 Flues and flue linings

The flue is a passage for conveying the smoke or discharge gases from an appliance to the external air. It may be formed by either a flue pipe or a flue liner within a chimney.

The chimney serving a class-1 appliance shall be lined with either clay flue linings to BS 1181, rebated or socketed flue linings made from kiln-burnt aggregate and high-alumina cement, or acid-resisting clay pipes to BS 65 & 540. The chimney may also be constructed of concrete flue blocks made of kiln-burnt aggregate and high-alumina cement (fig. 21.8). The flue cross-section should be such as will contain a circle of 175 mm diameter. The flue should also be surrounded and separated from any other flue in the chimney by a minimum thickness of 100 mm of solid material, excluding the thickness of the flue liner.

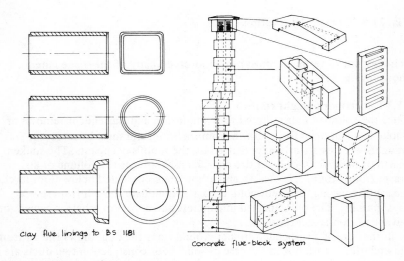

Clay flue linings to BS 1181

Concrete flue-block system

Fig. 21.8 Flue blocks and linings

Where flue pipes are used from an open fire, they should be cast iron to BS 41 or mild steel of 4.75 mm minimum thickness. If the appliance is not an open fire, then heavy-quality asbestos-cement piping to BS 835 may be used, providing that the first 1.8 m of the flue is constructed as for an open fire. The cross-sectional area of the flue pipe should be at least that of the outlet from the appliance

Older chimney constructions were parged (rendered) internally with a lime mortar. This parging or pargetting is subject to deterioration from the action of the flue gases and their condensate, leading to staining or smoke penetration through the chimney walls. This may be remedied by the use of a flexible flue liner.

To avoid down-draught problems or the likelihood of smoke being blown into a room through an open window, the outlet of any flue, exclusive of a

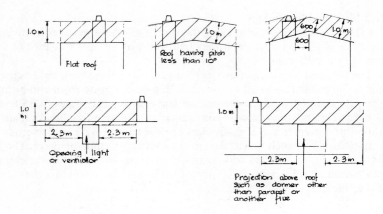

Fig. 21.9 Flue outlet location

chimney pot or terminal, must not be located in any of the shaded areas shown in fig. 21.9.

21.3 Underfloor-draught control
Since the volume of air required for combustion and subsequent removal of smoke from an open fire is drawn from the room and must be replaced, draughts were frequently experienced by the room's occupants. The sunken hearth or underfloor-draught fire considerably reduces the volume of air drawn from a room. The hearth and ashpit are constructed below floor level, the ashtray having sufficient volume to accommodate the ash from several days' burning. The pit is formed in concrete and a duct of asbestos cement or galvanised iron is incorporated.

In the case of a suspended timber ground floor the duct draws the air from the underfloor area, but in the case of solid floor construction two ducts are required to be laid at right angles to each other under the floor, terminating at the external walls with suitable protective gratings and internally in a balancing chamber from which air is drawn to the pit, thus avoiding the effects of suction pressure. The amount of air entering the pit is controlled by a disc at the pit end of the duct, operated by a lever at hearth level (fig. 21.10).

21.4 Gas fires and flues
a) *Fires* The principal types of gas fire are radiant and convector, the most common combining the two types and in addition incorporating a back-boiler which supplies hot water for both domestic and central-heating purposes. The modern natural convector is mounted on an external wall and has a room-sealed combustion chamber with a balanced flue passing through the wall to an outside flue terminal (fig. 21.11). The balanced flue consists of an incoming combustion-air duct and a flueway for the products of combustion.

164

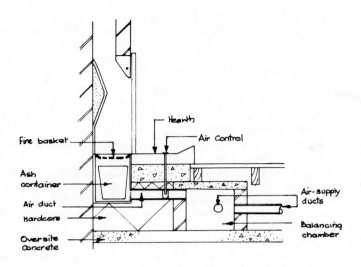

Fig. 21.10 Underfloor-draught provision

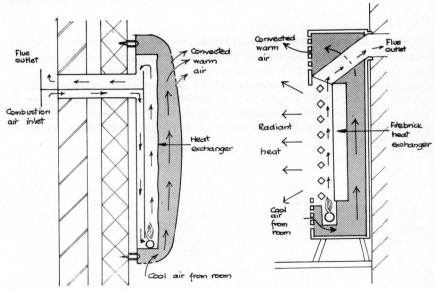

Fig. 21.11 Wall-mounted
convector

Fig. 21.12 Combined radiant
and convector heater

The combination unit (fig. 21.12) can be either hearth- or wall-mounted and is connected to a flue.

b) *Flues*   The main requirements for a flue to a class-2 appliance are

   i)   a minimum cross-sectional area of 12 000 mm^2 with no dimension less than 63 mm (the ratio of the side dimensions for rectangular flues to be a maximum of 6:1 for a flue serving a single gas fire, 5:1 for a single appliance other than a gas fire, and 1.5:1 for a main flue);

   ii)   flue pipes to be either glazed socket-and-spigot clay pipes to BS 65 & 540 jointed with high-alumina cement mortar, cast-iron socket-and-spigot pipes to BS 41 with an internal coating of acid-resistant vitreous enamel, sheet-metal flue pipes to BS 715, or stainless-steel pipes or asbestos-cement flue pipes to BS 835;

   iii)   flue pipes to be at least 50 mm from any combustible material;

   iv)   where a flue pipe passes through a floor, ceiling, roof, partition, or wall of combustible material, it should be enclosed in a non-combustible sleeve and have a 25 mm air space between it and the sleeve;

   v)   flue-pipe sockets should face upwards;

   vi)   chimneys should be lined with either acid-resisting tiles embedded in and pointed with high-alumina cement mortar, pipes as previously specified, or clay flue linings to BS 1181 jointed with high-alumina cement mortar;

   vii)   chimneys without linings may be constructed either of bricks or dense concrete blocks if they serve a single fire or of dense concrete blocks made of high-alumina cement and jointed with high-alumina cement mortar if they serve more than one appliance;

   viii)   the flue outlet should be fitted with a terminal which allows the free discharge of the products of combustion while minimising down-draught and preventing entry of extraneous material;

   ix)   the flue outlet should not be located in the shaded areas shown in fig. 21.13.

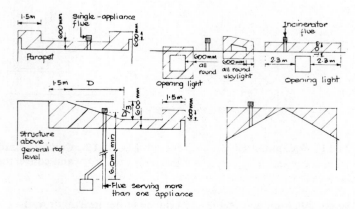

Fig. 21.13   Flue outlet location

166

For more detailed requirements, see clauses L14–22 of the Building Regulations.

21.5 Flue-block construction

The most common form of modern flue construction utilises flue blocks. The blocks, having the flue offset to one side (fig. 21.14) and a width equivalent to that of a brick, are easily bonded into a half-brick party or cavity wall built of either bricks or blocks. Special units cater for changes in direction or the change from flue block to pipe. This latter change may occur where there is a piped outlet from an appliance or, more commonly, above first-floor ceiling level in a two-storey domestic dwelling where the connection between blocks and the terminal is made by a length of flue pipe. This is done in order to avoid having to form a weatherproof chimney opening in the roof (fig. 21.14).

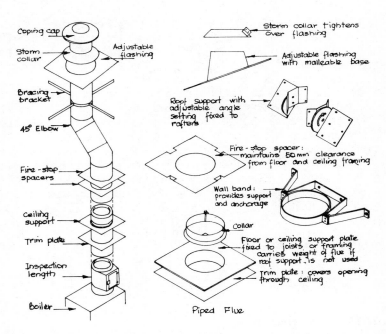

Fig. 21.14   Flue construction and terminal

The blocks should be laid with the female rebate upwards, so that any condensation that may be present in the flue will not permeate through an imperfect joint to the outer surface. High-alumina cement mortar is applied to the outside edge of the block only, leaving the inner rebate clear, and the next block is carefully lowered and pressed into position. Any extruded mortar should be immediately cleared away.

167

Terminals

In order to maintain uninterrupted roof lines on domestic pitched roofs, ridge terminals are frequently used. They are designed to blend with the ridge capping fig. 21.15(a). Alternatively, where a flue pipe projects above the roof surface, various terminals, illustrated in fig. 21.15(b), may be used.

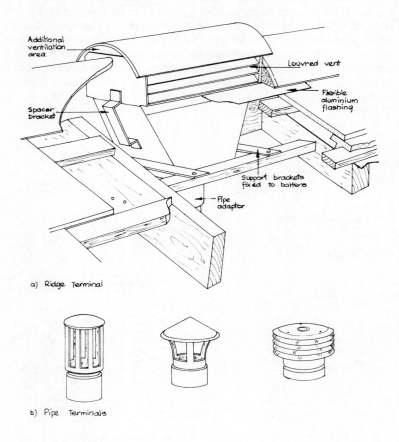

a) Ridge Terminal

b) Pipe Terminals

Fig. 21.15 Ridge terminals

Where the flue-block construction is taken through the roof in the form of a chimney, the flue blocks are masked by brickwork which is built off special flue-block corbel units and incorporates lead flashing (fig. 21.16) to prevent the entry of moisture at the junction of the roof and stack. The terminal in this case incorporates louvre units with a weathered capping unit (fig. 21.17).

In all cases, both flue blocks and terminals should not only comply with the Building Regulations but also be approved by the British Gas Corporation.

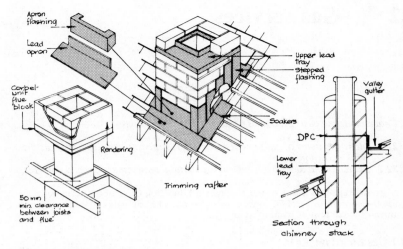

Fig. 21.16 Stack flashings

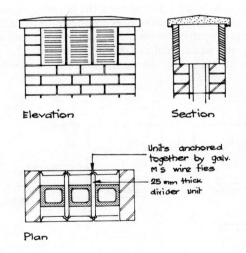

Fig. 21.17 Louvre units

169

22   Gas services

Understands the basic principles of gas services to buildings.

*22.1   Identifies items of equipment and space required by the Gas Boards at the
intake position.

*22.2   Sketches and describes a typical installation, indicating pipes and controls.

Acknowledgement is due to the Technician Education Council for permission to
use the content of the TEC units in this chapter. The council reserves the right to
amend the content of its units at any time

22.1 Gas Board intake

The gas service pipe into a building from the gas main should, ideally, enter
the building on the side nearest the main and terminate at a meter box on the
external wall. This box may be for metering the gas only or may incorporate
a prepayment facility. Typical meter sizes are shown in fig. 22.1. Access for
meter-reading purposes can cause problems for the Gas Board as well as the
Electricity Board, and an external meter cabinet similar to fig. 20.2 is one
solution. Another solution is for the meter to face the wall where a void has

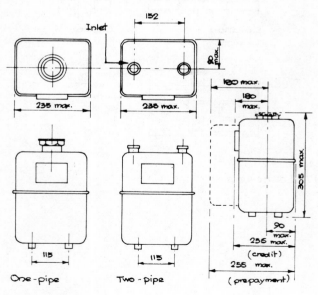

Fig. 22.1   Gas-meter sizes

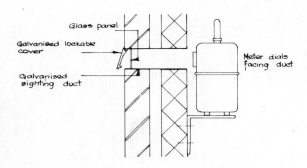

Fig. 22.2 Meter-reading facility

been created so that reading is carried out through a glass observation panel protected by a lockable metal cover (fig. 22.2).

In general, the base of the meter should be located at a height of 1.4 m above floor level (the minimum height is 760 mm), and there should be air space around the meter to minimise the likelihood of corrosion. The meter should also be located where it will not be damaged by external forces. The Gas Safety Regulations require that, in a building which has two or more storeys above ground level, a meter must not be installed in any part of the building which is on the route of the only means of escape in case of fire (e.g. on or under the stairway). In other buildings the meter should not be installed on the only escape route, but, where this location is the only practical position, the meter and its connections should be of fire-resisting construction or housed in a compartment whose top, bottom, and sides (including door) have a minimum half-hour fire resistance and whose door also is to be fitted with an automatic self-closing device. Alternatively, the service-pipe connection to the meter should incorporate a thermal cut-off device near the meter.

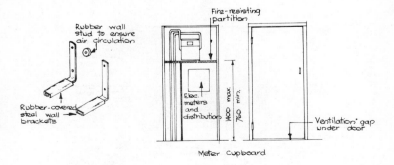

Fig. 22.3 Meter location

171

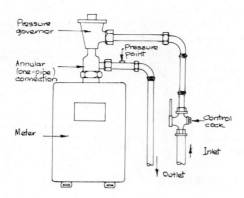

Fig. 22.4 Gas equipment

The items of equipment other than the meter at the intake position are shown in fig. 22.4 and consist of the following.

a) *Meter control*   A valve or cock adjacent to and on the inlet side of the meter which controls the supply of gas to the consumer.

b) *Meter (pressure or service) governor*   An outlet pressure governor which is designed to operate at an inlet pressure which could not be such as to balance a column of water exceeding 30 inches (762 mm) in height.

c) *Pressure point*   A fitting to which a pressure gauge can be attached for testing purposes.

Another item which maybe found at the intake position is

d) *Meter bypass* (fig. 22.5)   Consists of pipes, valves or cocks, and a bypass governor through which a supply of gas may pass directly from the service pipe to the installation pipe without passing through a meter. To prevent unlawful use of the bypass, the bypass valve should be sealed shut with a Gas Board seal.

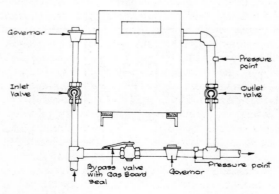

Fig. 22.5 Bypass detail

172

22.2 Typical gas installation

The installation pipe together with the fittings and appliances are the responsibility of the occupier of the premises. The installation pipe is defined as 'any pipe not being a service pipe for the use of gas on the premises of a consumer' and begins from the meter control.

As with other domestic services, the layout of an installation depends on the number, location, and type of appliances.

In assessing the layout requirements, careful consideration must be given to the volume of gas required by each appliance and the size of pipe required to provide such volume, taking into account the pipe lengths and fittings, nominal pipe bores ranging from 6 to 50 mm. A typical layout is indicated in fig. 22.6.

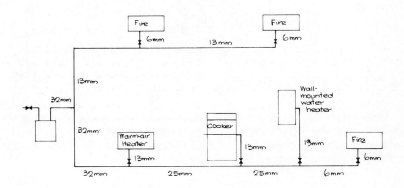

Fig. 22.6 Gas-installation layout

The most common installation-pipe materials are mild steel to BS 1387 grade B (medium) with screw joints, the connectors and bends also being of mild steel with other fittings such as tees being made from malleable iron; light-gauge copper to BS 2871, using capillary joints and copper fittings; lead pipes to BS 602 and 1085, with soldered joints; and chromium-plated brass for short plainly visible lengths.

The pipes should not generally be in contact with any finished surface and should be suitably supported by brackets or clips. Provision should be made to allow the removal of the various pipe lengths, and the pipe should be sleeved and fire-stopped where it passes through any wall or solid floor. Where pipes run under suspended timber floors across joists, the joists may be notched, providing the notch is not deeper than one sixth of the joist depth and is located between one sixth and one quarter of the span from the end of the joist. Pipes should not be run in cavities, nor should they be located near any heat source.

Pipes may be concealed in a wall by chasing, in which case the chase should be of sufficient depth to ensure that no part of the pipe is in contact with a plaster wall finish, since this might cause pipe corrosion. It is also preferable that the pipes be protected with a coating of red lead, or plastics-coated copper pipes be used.

The main control on a domestic service is the gas cock, preferably with a fan key (fig. 22.7) which drops through 90° when in the off position. The cock should be fitted as close as possible to the end of the pipe at its connection to the appliance. Where mobile appliances are used, such as gas pokers, a plug-in point should be used. This type of outlet incorporates a tap which automatically turns off the supply when the wandering lead is disconnected.

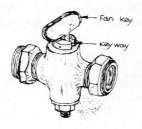

Fig. 22.7 Gas cock with fan key

When the installation pipework is complete, but before connections are made either at the meter or to the various appliances, the system is tested under air pressure to either 300 mm water gauge or twice the normal working pressure, whichever is the greater, using a manometer.

23   Underground drainage

Understands the construction of surface-water and soil drains and sewers over 100 mm diameter up to 225 m diameter, including brick and precast-concrete manholes up to 3 m deep.

23.1 *Explains the procedure for laying 100 mm diameter drains including concrete drain pipes, laying techniques, and testing.*

23.2 *Sketches and describes the collection of surface water into road gullies.*

23.3 *Explains and illustrates deep-manhole construction, including drop manholes and methods of testing.*

23.4 *Compares the use of brick and precast-concrete rings for deep manholes.*

23.5 *Describes the method of connecting large-diameter drains to the Local Authority sewer.*

23.6 *Describes safety precautions to be exercised in surface-water and foul drainage systems.*

Acknowledgement is due to the Technician Education Council for permission to use the content of the TEC units in this chapter. The council reserves the right to amend the content of its units at any time.

23.1 Drain laying
The laying of drains has already been described in volume 2 (chapter 22), while methods of testing have been covered in volume 1 (chapter 16).

23.2 Road drainage
Provision for adequate surface-water drainage from highways is essential if user facility is to be maintained. The surface water to be dealt with comes from the carriageway, footways, verges, and adjacent higher ground. Factors affecting the volume of water to be dealt with are considered in chapter 24.

Initially the rain water is directed off the trafficked hard surfaces by introducing falls across such surfaces. In the case of the carriageway, the fall (known as camber) to the gutter or channel may be in one direction across the lanes or in two directions from a central crown. The amount of fall across the carriageway or lanes depends on the anticipated rainfall intensity and the type of road surface, and should be sufficient to prevent any possibility of skidding or aquaplaning. A value of 1 in 40 is considered to be suitable for most purposes. The footway or verge also falls towards the kerb.

The gutter falls towards the gullies, usually having a high point mid-way between two gullies. The gullies are located between 25 and 40 m apart, depending upon the volume of surface water to be dealt with and the width of the highway (see volume 2, fig. 22.2).

There are various patterns of gulley grating and frame, designed to admit the maximum volume of water while preventing the entry of large debris such as sticks and stones. Typical details are shown in fig. 23.1.

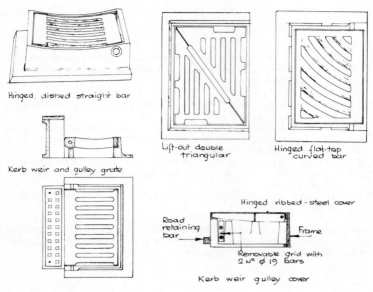

Fig. 23.1   Types of gulley frame and grating

The location of the gulley pot in relation to the kerb will depend upon the type of gulley selected. Small positional errors may be taken out within the two courses of engineering bricks which support the gulley frame from the pot (fig. 23.2).

23.3 Manhole construction
Where the depth of a manhole or inspection chamber is such that the clearance of blocked drains must be performed within the chamber rather than from ground level, there must be sufficient room for a person to carry out the operation. In order to reduce construction costs and at the same time provide as unobtrusive a surface cover as possible, a working chamber is formed at low level with an access shaft at high level. The shaft is sealed off at the surface by a cast-iron manhole cover. Where the manhole is created in the carriageway, the cover and frame should be heavy duty, sufficient to support the imposed traffic loading (fig. 23.3).

Manholes may be constructed of either brick or precast-concrete rings.

a) Brick manholes
The excavation for the drain or sewer is widened out to accommodate the manhole together with any necessary working space. A 225 mm thick in-situ

176

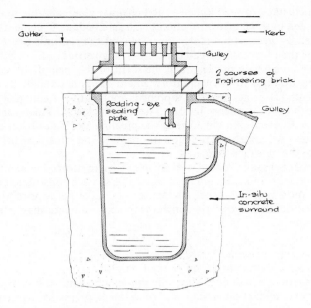

Fig 23.2 Section through gulley

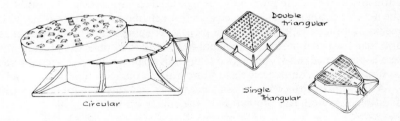

Fig. 23.3 Heavy-duty manhole cover

concrete base is cast some 50 mm below the invert level to provide a foundation for the walls and allow for the bedding in cement mortar of the channel sections within the manhole. The brick chamber is constructed of class-B engineering bricks to BS 3921 in 1:3 cement mortar, the wall thickness depending on the pressure of the surrounding ground, galvanised step irons being built into the wall as the work proceeds. Where a high water table is encountered, the chamber may require an external waterproof treatment to prevent the entry of subsoil water. A brick arch should be constructed over pipes whose diameter exceeds 150 mm so that the wall loading is not transferred to the pipes.

The main channel, formed in half-round channel pipes, and the branch channel, formed in three-quarter-section bends, are bedded in cement mortar and supported by weak concrete which is laid over the remaining base area. A benching is then formed of weak concrete, rising vertically from the edge of the channel to a height not less than the soffit of the main drain or sewer, before sloping upwards to the walls at a gradient of approximately 1 to 10. A granolithic or 1:1 cement mortar topping is applied to the concrete and floated smooth to form a dense hard surface on which a workman can stand and which, in the event of a blockage in the pipeline causing effluent to fill up the chamber, will resist water penetration and at the same time be self-draining once the blockage is cleared.

The chamber is usually roofed over by an in-situ reinforced-concrete slab, 150 mm thick, with an access hole provided. The shaft is constructed out of the chamber roof, usually one brick in thickness, and either capped by another in-situ r.c. slab or corbelled inwards to accommodate the surface cover and frame.

b) Precast-concrete manholes
Most precast-concrete manholes are circular on plan.

After excavation, a base of in-situ concrete may be formed similar to that for the brick manhole; alternatively, a purpose-made precast-concrete base unit incorporating the chamber and benching may be laid on a concrete blinding.

The chamber rings, manufactured in various standard heights and having step irons incorporated, are built up from the base. The rings are connected with an ogee joint, the lower joint being buttered with cement mortar before the next ring is positioned. The change from chamber to shaft is achieved by means of either a taper section or a precast reducing slab. The shaft rings are also manufactured in various standard heights so that, once the precast cover slab is positioned, only one or two courses of engineering brick are required to support the manhole frame and bring it up to the required surface level.

A 150 mm in-situ concrete surround to the manhole is required to provide additional strength and protection to the construction (fig. 23.4).

c) Backdrop manholes
See volume 1, chapter 16.

d) Testing manholes
Manholes should be tested for water tightness against the event of the main drain being blocked and the effluent backing up and filling the manhole. The test is normally carried out by filling the manhole with water and watching for any subsequent drop in the level. To achieve this, the length of drain downstream of the manhole must be plugged so that the plug can be removed after completing the test. In deep manholes, it must be borne in mind that the depth of water required for the manhole test may create pressures in excess of those for which the drain was designed. Pipes and joints should be carefully checked both during and after such tests.

178

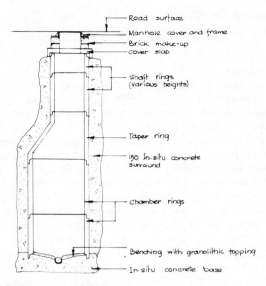

Fig. 23.4   Manhole construction

23.4 Comparison of manhole-construction methods

a) *Brick manholes*
    Advantages:
    i) shape can be adapted to suit site conditions,
    ii) variations in height easily accommodated,
    iii) materials can be transported to site in small units.
    Disadvantages:
    i) slow construction,
    ii) construction affected by weather,
    iii) high labour requirement,
    iv) brickwork must gain strength before testing and backfilling.

b) *Precast concrete*
    Advantages:
    i) speedy construction,
    ii) weather has little effect on construction,
    iii) low labour requirement.
    Disadvantages:
    i) crane required to position rings,
    ii) expensive if standard units are not used,
    iii) last-minute changes in depths difficult and expensive to accommo-
        date,
    iv) concrete surround expensive to provide, particularly if shuttering is
        used,

179

v) care required when forming holes through rings,
vi) breakage of rings may occur during delivery.

23.5 Sewer connection

The two main methods of connecting drains to sewers are by saddle or at a manhole. Since the sewer will be the responsibility of the local authority, the detailed requirements in terms of material quality and workmanship may vary from one authority to another.

a) *Saddle connection*   A saddle provides an easy form of connection to the sewer, provided there is the requisite access facility to the drain close by. The majority of local-authority sewers are to be found under the carriageway, and there are certain advantages to be gained from this form of connection, namely small volume of excavation and backfill and the speed of construction, thus reducing the interruption of traffic flow to a minimum. The crown of the existing sewer is exposed and a hole is carefully broken into it. The hole is then enlarged to the required size. The saddle is placed over the hole, the skirt being bedded in cement mortar with care being taken to ensure that no mortar enters the sewer. The drain is subsequently connected and the whole construction is surrounded in concrete (fig. 23.5).

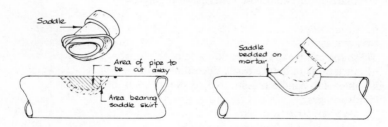

Fig. 23.5   Saddle connection

b) *Manhole connection*   Many local authorities will require a sewer connection to be made at a manhole. Where there is an existing manhole conveniently located, the connection will involve the cutting and reforming of the benching, breaking through the manhole wall, and subsequently making good once the pipework is complete. In circumstances where levels and drainage gradients dictate, the connection may also involve the construction of a backdrop or dropshaft. If there is no existing manhole available, the creation of a new manhole can be expensive since throughout the construction works the flow of effluent in the sewer must be maintained. This may, in certain circumstances, involve the pumping of the effluent overground between the manholes on either side of the proposed manhole.

180

23.6 Safety

There are two aspects of safety associated with drainage systems: initially during construction and subsequently in the operation and maintenance.

a) *During construction* The risks in this area are

    i) Trench collapse resulting from inadequate timbering.

    ii) Materials falling on to workmen in the trench because they were stacked too close to the edge.

    iii) Vehicles falling into the trench because of the lack or inadequate anchoring of stop boards.

    iv) Workmen or other people falling into the trench because of inadequate 'protective fencing'.

    v) Trench flooding during abnormal weather.

b) *Operational* Where work or inspection is being carried out in an existing drainage system, the risks to the workforce include

    i) Asphyxiation or poisoning resulting from gases or vapours present in the underground system. To overcome this problem, the system should be ventilated by opening not only the access manhole but also the adjacent manholes on both the upstream and downstream sides of the access, allowing at least half an hour to elapse prior to re-entry. The first person entering the system should be attached to a lifeline so that, if he should pass out, rescuers are not put at risk themselves. This implies that there should always be at least two people available on the surface during such work.

    ii) Flooding in a sewer may occur rapidly, and no reliance should be placed on weather forecasts. Immediate warning of imminent increase in flows can be provided by the workers on the surface.

    iii) Even after venting, pockets of gas may remain which apart from causing asphyxiation may also be explosive. Naked lights should, therefore, never be used.

    iv) Accidents from falls frequently occur. Only care on the part of the operatives and regular inspection and checking of step irons and ladders can reduce such incidents.

    v) When opening a manhole in a carriageway or footway, there should be adequate protective guarding placed around the opening so that neither vehicles or pedestrians can come to harm in the hole and, at the same time, the operatives are not injured by the passing highway users during entry and exit.

    vi) The possibility of infection from disease is always present, and operatives should be made aware of the dangers incurred through abrasions, food contamination, and touching their faces.

First-aid treatment and adequate washing facilities should therefore always be readily available.

24   Surface-water drainage

Calculates surface-water discharge and run off.

**24.1   *States that surface-water drainage calculations are based on catchment area, run-off factor, and intensity of rainfall in the area.*

**24.2   *Explains the meaning of the above terms and uses these terms for calculating the volume of water to be removed by use of the Lloyd-Davis formula and Road Note 35.*

Acknowledgement is due to the Technician Education Council for permission to use the content of the TEC units in this chapter. The council reserves the right to amend the content of its units at any time.

24.1 Basis of calculations

In order to design any surface-water sewer in terms of pipe size and gradient, the volume of water to be dealt with must first be established.

The simple formula for volume is length by breadth by depth, or area by depth. The area in this case is that part of the earth's surface which is draining into the sewer, and includes roads, paths, roofs, and gardens. However, the rain falling on a roof or a road is directly discharged into gutters and thence into the drainage system. The rain falling on gardens will be partially absorbed by the soil and will therefore affect the water table, which in turn may increase the flow in land drains, and some of that rain will eventually enter the sewer. For these reasons the area draining into a sewer must be modified to take account of the various surfaces on which the rain falls.

It is obvious that a plug is not pulled and a depth of water emptied into the sewer. The depth of water is really the amount of rain that falls; but, since the water in the sewer flows, this implies a time scale — volume per unit time — therefore the designer must take into account how much rain will fall in a given time.

24.2 Flow calculations

The area which is being drained by a surface-water sewer at a given point is termed the catchment area.

The *run-off factor* is the modification of the various component areas of the catchment with regard to their individual impermeabilities or percentage run-offs if such areas are known. Alternatively, an average value of the impermeability or run-off factor can be taken where the individual areas cannot be conveniently established but a housing density of N houses per hectare can readily be established. Opinions still differ as to the actual factors to be used, but fig. 24.1 gives an indication of their values.

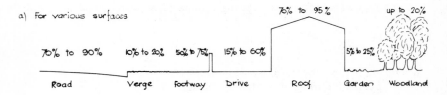

a) For various surfaces

Road — 70% to 90%
Verge — 10% to 20%
Footway — 50% to 75%
Drive — 15% to 60%
Roof — 70% to 95%
Garden — 5% to 25%
Woodland — up to 20%

b) For housing densities

| Houses per Hectare | Impermeability (%) | |
	Roseveare	Judson
10	20	18
20	30	25
30	45	33
50	68	50

Fig. 24.1 Run-off factors

The amount of rain falling or the intensity of rainfall together with the duration of storms of such intensity and the probability of their recurrence in a given number of years in a given geographical area can be obtained from the Meterorological Office, providing the designer gives the National Grid reference for the approximate centre of the area being considered.

At this stage the designer must consider whether to design the sewer to cope with a storm of given intensity which has a probability of occuring once every hundred years or to design for a storm which is likely to occur more frequently but with less intensity. He should take into account the damage which may be done by flooding as a result of all the rain-water not immediately draining away.

British Standard Code of Practice CP 301, 'Building drainage', recommends that an intensity of 50 mm per hour be assumed, but local factors must be taken into account. This intensity has a probability of occuring for a period of five minutes approximately once per year.

Obviously the volume of water to be removed increases as more branches are connected to the sewer, but, in calculations for the drainage of large areas, further factors must be taken into consideration such as the length of time it takes the rain-water to enter the sewer once it has fallen on the surface (approximately 2 minutes in urban areas) and the time (termed the time of concentration) taken for the water to reach the point in the system being considered once it has fallen on the surface, assuming that the pipe is flowing full bore.

For design using the 'rational' Lloyd-Davies formula, Road Note 35 suggests that a mean rate of rainfall during a storm be taken, with the storm duration being equal to the time of concentration of the catchment area at the point being considered. This design method is recommended only for small catchment areas where the time of concentration would not generally exceed 15 minutes.

The *Lloyd-Davis* formula gives the volume of rainwater to be dealt with:

$$Q = \frac{A_p \times i}{360} \text{ m}^3/\text{s (or cumecs)}$$

where A_p is the impermeable area in hectares,
  i is the intensity of rainfall in mm/h,
and   360 is a conversion factor for compatibility of units.
  Typical calculations are shown in fig. 24.2.

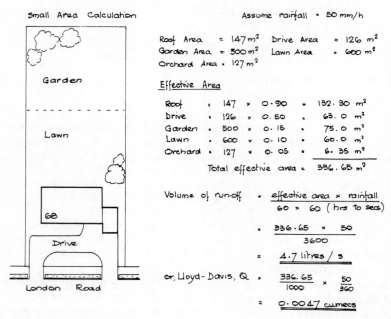

Fig. 24.2 Typical run-off calculation

25   Road construction

Understands the construction of flexible and rigid roads and pavements and methods of surfacing.

**25.1   *Distinguishes between flexible and rigid pavements.*
**25.2   *Explains the terminology used in road construction, including subgrade, sub-base, road base, road surfacing and formation level, and pavement.*
**25.3   *States that the strength of the pavement is built up from a suitable subgrade material.*
**25.4   *States that the subgrade must have a CBR value as specified in Road Note 29.*
**25.5   *Lists the manner in which the strength of subgrade may be achieved by compaction of in-situ material and imported fill.*
**25.6   *Lists the materials which are required in the construction of the road base and sub-base, including imported fill, bitumen, macadam, tarmacadam, and lean, mass, or reinforced concrete.*
**25.7   *Describes the method of pavement construction using materials in 25.6.*
**25.8   *Draws cross-sections showing kerbs, channels, cross-falls, longitudinal joints, and pavement construction.*

Acknowledgement is due to the Technician Education Council for permission to use the content of the TEC units in this chapter. The council reserves the right to amend the content of its units at any time.

25.1 Pavements

The pavement is the whole of the paved area of a road, and it includes both the carriageway and the footway.

A road must be classified by the amount of traffic which uses it (light, medium, or heavy) or by the form of construction. There are two distinct forms of construction, namely flexible and rigid.

a)   *Flexible pavement*   This consists of a number of layers of various materials which distribute the loads applied by a vehicle's wheels to the subgrade without any permanent deformation.

b)   *Rigid pavement*   This consists of a concrete slab resting on a thin granular base. The slab may be reinforced, depending on the loading, which is designed to be spread over a large area of the subgrade.

25.2 Terminology

A carriageway or pavement consists of several components which are shown diagrammatically in fig. 25.1:

a)   *Subgrade*   The natural ground on which the road is constructed.

b)   *Formation*   The surface of the subgrade from which the road construction begins.

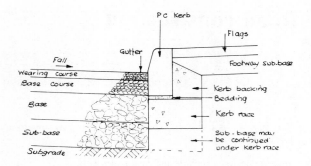

Fig. 25.1 Carriageway terminology

c) *Sub-base* A bedding of material laid on the subgrade to improve drainage, provide frost protection, and improve the strength of the subgrade.
d) *Road base* The main foundation and load spreader in the construction.
e) *Surfacing* Consists of a base and wearing coat or courses, which together must withstand the immediate stresses imposed on them by traffic and provide good skid resistance. It.should also provide weather protection to the foundation without retaining moisture for too long on the surface.

25.3 Pavement strength
The strength of a pavement can only be as good as that of the natural ground on which it rests and the ability of the pavement foundation to transmit loads safely.

As the loading on a carriageway can be both static and dynamic, this increases the design problems. The results of roads now being subjected to traffic conditions for which they were not designed can regularly be seen in both town and country.

A designer must not only predict the anticipated traffic usage of a given carriageway in terms of volume and weight but must also ensure that the materials incorporated into the design from subgrade upwards will be able to fulfil their particular function for many years.

25.4 Subgrade strength
The thickness of a pavement construction depends on the strength of the subgrade. This strength is assessed using the California Bearing Ratio (CBR) — see section 1.5 — and is used to determine the thickness of the sub-base using design charts contained in Road Note 29 (HMSO, 1970) — see fig. 25.2.

25.5 Subgrade requirements
The higher the CBR value of the subgrade, the more economic will be the construction. The CBR value may be improved, or achieved in the case of a poor subgrade, in a variety of ways, as follows.

Type of soil	Plasticity index (%)	CBR (%)	
		Depth of water-table below formation level	
		More than 600 mm	600 mm or less
Heavy clay	70	2	1
	50	2.5	2
Silty clay	30	5	3
Sandy clay	20	6	4
	10	7	5
Sand (poorly graded)	—	20	10
Sand (well graded)	—	40	15
Sandy gravel (well graded)	—	60	20

Fig. 25.2 Typical subgrade CBR values (extract from Table 3, Road Note 29)

a) Provision of *sub-soil drainage*. Most soils are weaker when saturated than when dry. Their moisture content, resulting from seasonal fluctuations in the water-table level or ground-water seepage, may be reduced by means of cut-off drains alongside the construction, and these should be designed to prevent the water table rising to within 600 mm of the formation level. In the case of seepage from the pavement, the application of a sealing coat of hot tar or bitumen to the subgrade surface will reduce the effect of downward moisture movement.

b) The reduction in moisture content will also assist in reducing the effect of ground heave caused by frost action.

c) *Compaction* of the subgrade will improve the density of the soil and hence the CBR value.

d) Where the subgrade is very weak, the soil may be excavated and replaced with good-quality *imported fill*, which should be adequately compacted in layers.

e) With certain types of subsoil, an alternative to (d) above is the use of *soil-stabilisation techniques* which involve the mixing of cement and/or p.f.a. with pulverised soil to a minimum depth of 75 mm and compacting the mix in layers not exceeding 200 mm deep.

25.6 Road-construction materials

a) *Sub-base*
   i) Suitably graded sands, gravels, and crushed rock containing a low percentage of fine material
   ii) Ash or crushed slag

b) *Road base* The material must have a compacted CBR value of 80%, not be affected by frost, and remain stable in water. Suitable materials include:

      i)   Crushed rock
     ii) Dry lean concrete (1:15 mix)
   iii) Dry-bound macadam   flexible
    iv) Water-bound macadam
     v) Bitumen macadam
    vi) Grade-30 concrete (mass or reinforced) – rigid

c) *Base course*
      i)   Dense bitumen macadam
     ii) Dense tarmacadam   flexible
   iii) Coated macadam
    iv) Hot-rolled asphalt

d) *Wearing course*
      i)   Dense bitumen macadam
     ii) Medium-textured tarmacadam   flexible
   iii) Hot-rolled asphalt
    iv) Cold asphalt
     v) Air-entrained concrete (monolithic with base) – rigid

25.7 Pavement construction

a) *Flexible*   After a suitable CBR value for the subgrade has been achieved and the surface has been sealed, the sub-base is laid and is consolidated by roller, the weight of which will be dependent on both the sub-base and subgrade materials. It is at this stage that the cross-falls in the carriageway are introduced and kerb construction is carried out. The kerb provides the limits of the construction and is frequently used to provide subsequent level datums.

    The road base is laid in one or more layers, depending on thickness, each layer being well consolidated by a roller, the laying being carried out by a self-propelled spreader and finisher (fig. 25.3) in the case of macadam. The base course is laid by the same machine in one pass and is satisfactorily consolidated by roller(s) to provide a plane surface. The wearing coat is subsequently laid in one coat – ensuring that the base-coat surface is free from clay, excess tar, or other extraneous matter – and is rolled to a plane surface finish. A topping of bitumen-coated

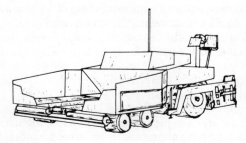

Fig. 25.3 Road pavior

chippings is immediately laid, by a spreader, on top of a hot-rolled asphalt wearing coat. When laying new material abutting on freshly laid or old material, care should be taken to ensure good adhesion between joints by cutting back to a dense full-depth vertical face and painting the face with hot bitumen or bitumen emulsion.

Typical constructions are shown in fig. 25.4.

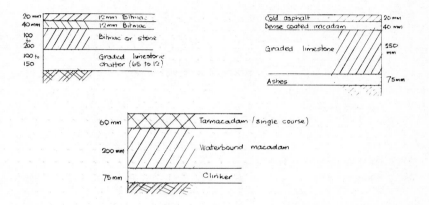

Fig. 25.4 Typical flexible-pavement construction

b) *Rigid* After consolidation of the sub-base, a blinding layer of fine material is laid and rolled to provide a smooth surface on which is laid a sliding layer of polythene sheeting. The concrete slab may be laid by hand in a similar manner to that described in volume 2, section 5.6, or, in the case of large constructions, by a concrete train. The joints in the reinforced-concrete slab are shown in fig. 25.5, their location being shown in fig. 25.6.

In city areas where there is a poor quality subgrade, problems of differential settlement, or shallow service trenches, a reinforced-concrete base may be laid with a flexible base course and a wearing course of rolled asphalt. In other situations, where the surface of the concrete is to be the wearing surface, the concrete surface should be air-entrained (approximately 4% volume of air) to a minimum depth of 50 mm to improve the resistance of the concrete to damage from frost and de-icing salts.

25.8 Road details

Cross-sectional details showing construction of kerbs, cross-falls, and channel falls are given in figs 25.7 and 25.8.

189

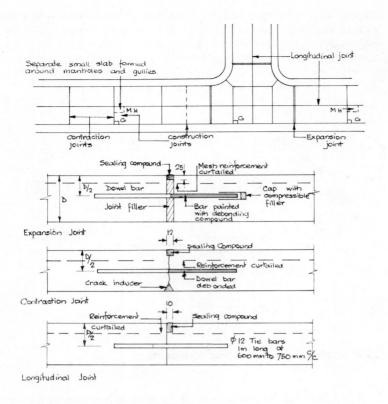

Fig. 25.5 Concrete-road joint details

Joint type	Spacing
Longitudinal	Slab width not to exceed 4.5 m.
Expansion	60 m (72 m) max. for unreinforced slabs of 200 m or greater thickness.
	40 m (48 m) max. for unreinforced slabs less than 200 mm thick.
	39 m (48 m) for reinforced slabs.
Contraction (similar to the induced joint)	5 m (6 m) max. intervals between expansion joints in unreinforced slabs.
	13 m (16 m) ditto for reinforced slabs.

Fig. 25.6 Joint spacing. Figures in brackets indicate values where the concrete has a limestone aggregate

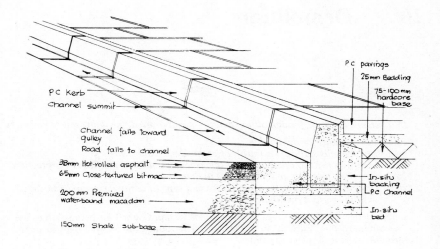

Fig. 25.7 Road cross-section

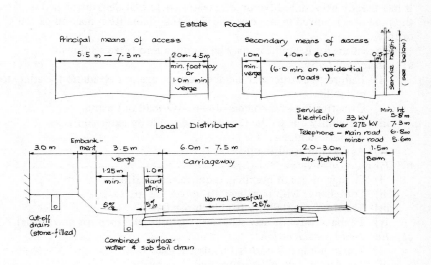

Fig. 25.8 Cross-fall details

26   Demolition

Understands the need for demolition and the methods used, including safety measures.

*26.1 Lists reasons for demolition.
*26.2 Understands statutory controls affecting demolition work.
*26.3 Identifies risks to operatives and the general public and methods of protection.
*26.4 Describes methods and procedures to demolish.
*26.5 Describes and illustrates the need for and type of temporary works associated with the various methods.

Acknowledgement is due to the Technician Education Council for permission to use the content of the TEC units in this chapter. The council reserves the right to amend the content of its units at any time.

26.1 Reasons for demolition

It has already been stated (volume 2, section 4.1) that demolition is one of the processes involved in site clearance and that demolition may be partial or total.

The reasons for demolition may be grouped into three sections.
a) *Structural failure*
    i)   Failure of a structural member, due to age or degradation, leading to instability.
   ii) Overstressing of members, due to overload or misuse.
  iii) Instability due to the removal or damage by external forces of support members.
  iv) As (iii) but resulting from fire.
b) *Progress of society*
    i)   Change of use of building, requiring adaptation.
   ii) Compliance with new legislation (e.g. on fire exits).
  iii) Social unacceptability (e.g. high-rise flats).
  iv) To make way for new schemes (e.g. redevelopment or new roads).
c) *Economic considerations*
    i)   The building has outlived its useful life.
   ii) The building would cost too much to repair.
  iii) Uneconomic land use.

26.2 Statutory controls

Before any demolition work is carried out, section 29 of the Public Health Act 1961 requires notice to be given to the local authority (in England and Wales) or the district surveyor (Inner London area) or a warrant to be obtained from the buildings authority of the relevant Scottish burgh or county. Planning permission may also be required in the case of listed buildings.

Before demolition works are begun, notice must be given to all the statutory undertakings, i.e. electricity, gas, water, telephone, and other bodies responsible for local or community services such as district heating and radio and television land lines.

Where the demolition works are to take longer than six weeks, the Health and Safety inspectorate must be informed, and the local fire brigade should be consulted where controlled burning is proposed.

Other statutory controls applying to demolition work are more specific in nature. These include

a)   the Explosives Acts 1875 and 1923,
b)   the Clean Air Act 1968,
c)   the Asbestos Regulations 1969,
d)   the Highways Act 1959,
e)   the Construction Regulations 1961 and 1966.

Part X of the General Provisions of the Construction Regulations 1961 covers the various aspects of safety and supervision related specifically to demolition works and, together with British Standard Code of Practice CP 94 and Department of Environment Health and Safety at Work booklet 6E, provides a guide to good practice.

Indemnity insurance (usually provided by the demolition contractor), although not statutory, should cover against third-party loss in respect of property loss, damage or fire, and personal injury.

26.3 Risks and protection

Demolition is one of the most dangerous of all operations in the construction industry, and an appreciation of the risks involved is therefore essential.

The most important risk − that to human life − can be divided between the operatives and the general public.

a) Operatives

   i)   *Falls* − from unsafe sections of work, through holes created for debris to pass through, overbalancing, and tripping in unlit stairways and corridors.

  ii) *Falls of material* − being hit by falling debris.

 iii) *Unintentional collapse* of the whole or part of the structure − due to insufficient temporary support, removal of structurally important members, overloading of structural members, or wind and other climatic effects.

 iv) *Fires* − caused by friction, flame-cutting equipment, electrical short circuits, and loss of control of small deliberate fires.

  v) *Explosions* − flame-cutting of empty volatile-liquid containers and firing of rubbish containing hidden gas cylinders.

 vi) *Lifting operations* − incorrect procedures adopted both for physical and mechanical operations.

vii) *Services* Failure to cut and seal off all services — particularly gas, electricity, and sewers — can create many health hazards.
viii) *Injuries* — to head, eyes, hands, and feet.
ix) *Plant and equipment* — should be operated by competent trained personnel.

Protection is best afforded by the provision of suitable safety clothing in the form of helmets, boots, goggles, gloves, and jackets. When working in areas where he is likely to fall, an operative should wear a safety harness attached to a safe anchorage. Debris should be channelled down chutes or dropped within the building envelope and removed before any structural overload occurs. An awareness, by preliminary survey, of the structure and its contents together with any surrounding buildings will enable a safe sequence of operations to be prepared and adhered to. It is imperative that there is constant supervision by persons with a thorough knowledge of both demolition work and construction principles who will be able to foresee the attendant problems.

b) General public
Demolition work, like construction work, attracts interest; but, for its own safety, the public must be protected, and this protection should prevent damage from items similar to those listed in (a) above. The adage that 'prevention is better than cure' is never truer than in this case, the prevention being in the form of hoardings, ideally 2.4 m high, totally enclosing the site. Where people, vehicles, or other buildings are in close proximity, protection from falling objects is provided by fans (fig. 26.1) erected at first-floor level (and alternate floor levels for higher buildings).

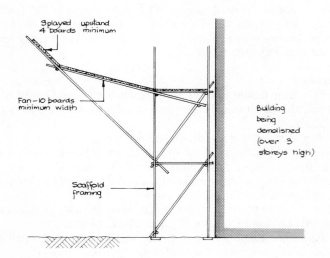

Fig. 26.1 Fans

194

In built-up areas, noise can cause problems, and BS 5228 provides a code of practice for the control of noise.

Dust, caused by crumbling plaster and mortar, should be controlled by periodic spraying with water, to reduce air pollution; while favourable low-wind conditions should be awaited prior to any controlled burning, to prevent offence from smoke. The local authority should also be contacted to ascertain any requirements relating to smoke-control areas. Fires should be extinguished well before workmen leave the site, to avoid problems of any possible flare up.

26.4 Demolition methods

The method of demolishing a particular structure will be determined by
the size of the building,
its type and method of construction,
its location within the site boundary,
the distance away from surrounding buildings,
the amount of recoverable/reusable materials and components,
the expertise of a particular contractor,
the amount of time available for the execution of the work.

a) Hand demolition

This is used where salvage material is valuable and in decent condition, where only partial demolition is required, or where there is severe site restriction. The method is slow, since it involves operatives using hand tools such as sledge-hammers, picks, pneumatic drills with points, and spades.

The work should be programmed and will generally be carried out in the reverse order to that of the building's construction. The debris should only be allowed to fall freely to the ground internally, or externally where there is

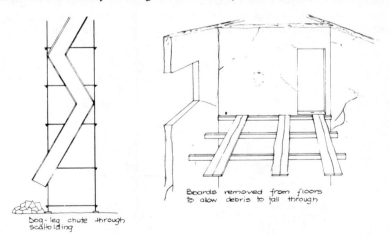

Dog-leg chute through scaffolding

Boards removed from floors to allow debris to fall through

Fig. 26.2   Fall of debris

195

no risk of damage to public or property (see fig. 26.2). Internal openings in floors should be created for the free fall of the debris without affecting the structural stability of the building. Alternatively, chutes or skips should be used.

Large structural members of reinforced concrete or steel should be supported by a crane and, when released, lowered to the ground.

Fragmentation is carried out by a number of methods, as follows, the main object being quickly to reduce the building to a heap of rubble.

b) Demolition ball
This method uses a cast-steel or concrete mass suspended from a luffing jib crane or drag-line excavator. The three techniques used are (i) vertical drop, (ii) swinging the ball forward in line with the jib of the machine, and (iii) swinging the ball by slewing the jib of the machine.

The hoist-rope connection to the ball should be fitted with an antispin device or, in the case of a drag-line machine, the drag rope should always be attached. Care should be taken to prevent the ball and ropes becoming entangled in the building. The jib head should always be at least 3 m above the height of the building, and the machine cab should be strong enough to withstand flying debris, with additional protection to the windows, which should be shatter-proof.

c) Pusher arm
The arm is usually a steel or large-section timber beam, the former being a special attachment to a hydraulic backactor (fig. 26.3), the latter being housed in a special shoe located on the top of the bucket of an excavator/loader. The machines should operate only on firm level ground, the arm being applied near to the top of the structure to be demolished, and the cab of the machine should be protected as previously described.

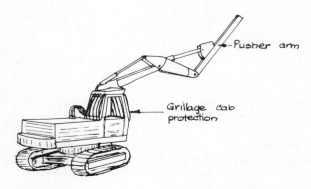

Fig. 26.3 Pusher arm

196

d) Pulling rope

A 38 mm minimum-diameter wire rope is wrapped round a section of a structure and pulled either by winch or by tractor, with the object of removing structural stability to induce collapse. The technique should not be used on masonry structures exceeding 20 m high, and the length of rope from the structure to the pulling force should be at least twice the height of the building being demolished. Because of the high stresses involved, damaged ropes must not be used, and no person should be in front of the pulling force for a distance of at least three quarters of the rope length, to prevent accidents from the whip-lash effect of any rope failure.

e) Explosives

The most impressive of all demolition techniques, the use of explosives is restricted to specialists holding the necessary licences. Before blasting, the police should be informed so that livestock and people may be kept at a safe distance, and the service authorities should be informed so that they are aware of possible damage to their facilities which may be caused by shock waves.

This form of demolition provides total collapse by removing the structural support at or near ground level, or progressive collapse by linking a series of charges by delayed fuses throughout the height of the building. In the former case the direction of the collapse and the fall of debris must be controlled, while the latter usually restricts the fall of debris to within a very short distance of the building plan area.

Blast mats or baffles should be used to protect surrounding properties from shock, vibration, and flying debris.

Other specialist techniques include:

f) Gas-expansion burster

This consists of a steel cylinder inserted into an existing or prepared cavity. The cylinder contains chemicals or liquefied gas which, when ignited by an electrical charge, expand rapidly with considerable force, causing fracture and fragmentation of the surrounding structural mass.

g) Grab

The building is demolished by the grab 'biting' the fabric down from high level. This prevents a build-up of debris at low level, since the 'bites' can be immediately loaded on to waggons.

h) Hydraulic burster

This consists of a steel cylinder with a number of pistons which are forced radially outwards against the surrounding structure under hydraulic pressure. It is similar to the gas-expansion burster in that flying debris is reduced to a minimum.

j) Thermal reaction

Structural-steel members are exposed and surrounded by a mixture of metal oxides and a reducing agent. When the mixture is electronically ignited, a large amount of heat is given off, causing the steel to become plastic. The weight of the structure above, or a small additional force from tensioned wires, is sufficient to create imbalance and subsequent collapse of the building.

k) Thermic lance

Structural concrete and steel members are cut by intense heat. The tip of the thermic lance, which consts of steel rods packed in a steel tube, is preheated so that, when oxygen is passed down the tube, an oxygen/iron reaction is started which produces the intense heat. Care must be taken to support the surrounding structure and protect the operatives, since the heat may reduce the load-bearing capacity of adjoining members.

In all demolition work it is essential to remember the ten S's:
- i) Survey the work carefully.
- ii) Stabilise the adjoining buildings.
- iii) Services should be disconnected or modified.
- iv) Secure the site to prevent unauthorised access.
- v) Specialists should be consulted at an early stage.
- vi) Salvage important materials.
- vii) Small number of operatives on site.
- viii) Supervise constantly.
- ix) Structural-collapse methods are economic when practical and safe.
- x) SAFETY is the vital aim.

26.5 Temporary works

Shoring of adjoining structures to provide stability during demolition works may be required (see section 7.3), while safe access and working platforms can be provided by scaffolding (see chapter 8).

Other temporary works associated with demolition include the restraint and support of structural members when they are being cut, to avoid collapse if deliberate-collapse methods are not being used (see fig. 26.4).

Where arched structures are being demolished, temporary centring may be required to prevent collapse as a result of removing the spandrel infilling; and lateral restraint, in the form of temporary bracing, should be provided where intermediate spans are removed (see fig. 26.4).

Buildings containing basements or cellars which are not filled by the demolition rubble should be securely fenced.

Weatherproofing of adjoining or adjacent buildings exposed by demolition can be either of a temporary or a permanent nature, depending on the reason for the demolition works. Temporary protection may be provided by scaffolding or a lightweight metal frame covered by tarpaulins, plastics sheeting, or corrugated roofing sheets; while permanent protection is usually in the

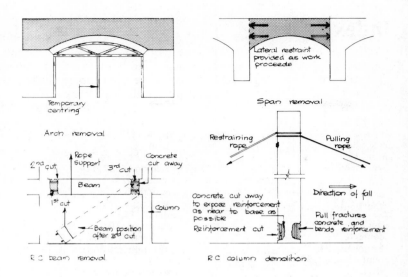

Fig. 26.4 Temporary restraint

form of either an additional half-brick outer skin, cement rendering, or vertical slate or tile hanging.

Internal alteration works giving rise to demolition works may be sectioned off from other areas by the erection of temporary stud partitions clad with plastics sheet, hardboard, or plywood, so as to restrict their effects on surrounding accommodation.

199

Index

air cock, 145
angle fillet, 26
apron, 169
auger, 3, 45

bar chart, 13
base course, 188
beam
  concrete, 91
  formwork, 94
  reinforcement, 92
  steel, 85
bellows joint, 129
Bentonite, 65
bittiness, 140–2
bleeding, 140–2
blistering, 140–2
blockboard, 137
bloom base, 83
blooming, 140–2
bolts, 80
  holding-down, 85
  roof, 100
borehole, 2
bracing
  shoring, 67
  window, 48

California bearing ratio, 6, 186
carriers, 21
catchment, 182
cat ladder, 100
chalking, 140–2
chimney, 163
chipboard, 138
circuit breaker, 151
cissing, 140–2
cleat, 67, 84
column
  concrete, 90
  steel, 85
concrete
  additives, 29
  floors, 121
  no-fines, 114
  pavement, 189

piles, 41
plant, 52
prestressed, 58
reinforced, 87, 114
stairs, 133
waterproof, 29
watertight, 28
conduit, 152
connectors, 103
construction joints, 29, 190
Construction Regulations, 17, 30, 71,
  193
counterfort, 64
cover
  concrete, 90
  manhole, 176
crazing, 140–2
crib, 66
cross-walls, 110
curing, 28, 57
curtaining, 140–2

demolition, 192
dewatering, 49
diaphragm wall, 65
doors, 124–7
door stop, 126
dowel bars, 47, 190
drains
  land, 26, 50
  surface-water, 175, 182
drop shaft, 180
drop system, 147
dumpling, 23

eaves, 101
efflorescence, 140–3
electricity, 149
excavation
  basement, 23
  closed, 23
  open, 23
  protection, 32
  safety, 31
  trench, 23
excavators, 19

fan, 194
fender, 160
fibreboard, 138
fill, 32, 33, 137
fire, gas, 164
fireback, 160
fire doors, 126
fireplace, 158
fire resistance, 87, 171
flaking, 140–3
flashings, 169
floors, 120
flue, 163, 166
formation, 185
formwork, 93
  stairs, 134
  table, 94
  ties, 96
foundations
  piled, 39
  strip, 47
fuse-board, 152
fuses, 149, 151

gas, 170
glazing bead, 129
governor, 172
grading test, 8
grillage, 67
grinning, 140–3
guides, 36
gulley, 175
gusset
  base, 82
  plate, 99
gutter, 175

hardboard, 138
health and safety, 17, 100, 193
hearth, 159
heating systems, 144–8

industrialised building, 114

ladders, 73, 77
ladder system, 147
laminboard, 138
ledger, 71, 134
linings
  flue, 163
  wall, 136
Lloyd-Davies formula, 183
loading coat, 26
lugs, 116

manhole, 176, 179
mass–haul diagram, 19
meter
  electricity, 149
  gas, 170
microbore heating system, 144

needle, 48, 67

one-pipe system, 144

paintwork, 140–3
partitions, 128
patent glazing, 117
pavement, 185
piles
  bored, 44, 65
  concrete, 41
  driven, 40
  sheet, 35
  steel, 40
  timber, 40
plant
  compaction, 33
  concrete, 52
  demolition, 195–8
  piling, 37
  planning, 11
  pumps, 50
  selection, 18
plasterboard, 136
plate bearing test, 6
poling boards, 23
pressure bulb, 2
propping, 48
puddle flange, 30
purlin, 100
putlog, 71

radiators, 144
rakers, 35, 68
raking struts, 23
reinforcement, 87, 134
retaining walls
  backfill, 33
  functions, 61
  types, 63
rider, 68
ridge, 101
ridge terminal, 168
ring main, 155
road base, 186
roof coverings, 100
roof trusses, 98

rotary boring, 3
run-off factor, 182

saddle, 180
saponification, 140–3
scaffolding, 71
self-centring, 121
sewer, 180
shims, 85
shores
  dead, 66, 69
  flying, 66, 70
  raking, 66, 70
shoring, 48, 66, 199
site personnel, 16
slips, 107
small-bore heating systems, 144
soaker, 169
soil investigation, 2, 19, 39, 46
soil samples, 3–4
soil stabilisation, 187
sole-plate, 68
spine beam, 133
stage programme, 15
stairs, 132
standard, 71
standard penetration test, 6
steelwork, 79, 99
stringer, 133
sub-base, 186
subgrade, 185
sulphate-content test, 8
surfacing, 186

tanking, 26
temporary accomodation, 11

temporary services, 12
thermostat, 146
throat, 161
timbering, 48
topsoil, 33
transom, 71, 118
tremie pipe, 65, 97
trestles, 73, 77
trial hole, 2
two-pipe system, 144

unconfined compression test, 8
underpinning, 46

valves, 145
vane test, 7
vapour barrier, 109
verge, 101

waist, 134
walls
  cross-, 110
  panel, 97, 106
  panelling, 129
  retaining, 61
wash boring, 3
water exclusion, 25
water stop, 30
water table, 19, 26, 39, 49
wearing course, 188
welding, 81
windows, 116
wood-wool slabs, 138
wrinkling, 140–3